THE PRINCETON REVIEW

Math Smart
for Business

D0094251

THE PRINCETON REVIEW

Math Smart for Business

CULTIVATING A SIX-FIGURE VOCABULARY

BY PAUL WESTBROOK

RANDOM HOUSE, INC.
New York 1999
http://www.randomhouse.com

Princeton Review Publishing, L.L.C.
2315 Broadway
New York, NY 10024
E-mail: info@review.com

ISBN 0-679-77356-8

Editor: Amy Zavatto
Designer: Illeny Maaza
Production Coordinator: Matthew Reilly
Illustrations: The Production Department of The Princeton Review

Manufactured in the United States of America on recycled paper.

9 8 7 6 5 4 3 2

Acknowledgments

Special thanks to Karin Halperin for her efforts to improve my writing.

Many thanks to Jeremy Gold who has been trying to improve my understanding of math over many years. Thanks to Ransom Widmer for his assistance and the other members of the Ridgewood Math Group, Andrea Holmes and Bimla Shukla. Thanks to Larry Smiley and Martin Shapiro for their help.

I also want to thank in particular Evan Schnittman, Editor-in-Chief at Princeton Review for his overall direction and Amy Zavatto, Editor of this book at Princeton Review, for her cool editorial hand. Additional thanks to Jon Spaihts for his editing assistance.

CONTENTS

Part III

Introduction

In my financial and retirement planning seminars, I teach certain aspects of math. I have also discussed and tutored more advanced subjects in math over the years. These experiences have led me to three conclusions:

- Math continues to baffle most people

- Math is known but unused by many people

- Math is exciting to a few people

These conclusions divide people neatly into three groups according to their level of comfort with math: the timid, the math-friendly, and the adventuresome. Each of this book's three sections is directed at one of these three groups. My secret plan is to improve everyone's understanding of math. If you feel pushed to know more, that's quite deliberate.

Part I: For the math-timid, this section can give readers a greater understanding of basic concepts. A solid understanding of the basics is the first step toward math power.

Part II: For the math-friendly, especially those who don't use it frequently enough, this section is meant as a handy reference. The subjects of present and future value and statistics are very important to you.

Part III: For the math-adventuresome, this section summarizes some advanced topics that may challenge you. This is simply a starting point. The subjects in this section are timely and relevant to our modern technology. The future belongs to the math-powerful.

How To Use This Book

If you know your mathematical skill level or want to know about a specific math area, go right to the relevant section. If you're looking for a specific business application, check the index. There's also a chapter on graphs and the presentation of math information.

If you want a definition, there's a comprehensive glossary in the back of the book. It includes over 270 definitions, including such things as the values of pi and *e*, and the Roman numerals—check it out.

A Final Word

Math is only a tool. As you grow more familiar with math, you'll become less likely to avoid it or misuse it. It's no more mysterious than any other discipline, after all, and it surely is not beyond your capabilities. It's time we got over our intimidation and started to use math to better control our *business* world.

PART I

CHAPTER 1

Percentages

If you're single and making $35,000 a year and the taxes you had to pay were $8,500 (including federal, FICA, and state income taxes), what percentage are those taxes of your salary? *Percentages* are all around us. The stock market rose only 1.31% in 1994, but increased by 37.43% in 1995. In 1970, fewer than 15% of drivers used seat belts, while 66% did in 1996. Bob Dole campaigned on reducing taxes 15%. The vote tally of the 1996 presidential election was finalized at: Clinton 49.1%, Dole 40.9%, and Perot 8.5%. Historically, the dividend rate for common stock is about 3.5% of the stock price, but at the end of 1996 it was as low as 2%.

IS EVERYTHING A PERCENTAGE?

PURPOSE

Why do we use percentages, anyway? Because they add meaning to numbers. They show differences and comparisons that raw numbers can't. They also communicate quickly and pointedly. Often, when you're studying numerical information, you're looking for a trend; comparing percentages over time makes it easier to see the direction of change, if one exists.

See for yourself. Consider the following two paragraphs and see how percentages add meaning:

1. At the turn of the century, in 1900, the population of the U.S. was about 76 million, including 3 million people over the age of 65. Today, as we approach another century, we have a population of about 263 million, including about 32 million people over 65.

2. At the turn of the century, in 1900, the population of the U.S. was about 76 million. Some 3 million of these people were over the age of 65, making up about 4% of the total population. Today, as we approach another century, we have a population of about 263 million. About 12% of the population or 32 million people are over 65. It's projected that by 2030, older Americans will make up about 20% of the population.

Naturally, the actual numbers are useful themselves. The raw numbers of 3 million versus 32 million older Americans indicate the expansion of this age group over the decades. But the total population has grown as well, making the significance of these numbers unclear. When you express the numbers as percentages, a clearer picture emerges. We can then see that people over the age of 65 are not only more predominant, but they also constitute a bigger share of the population. This could give them considerably greater clout in our society, a fact of great importance to manufacturers, advertisers, politicians, and many others. Percentages make the relationships between numbers clear, which can provide valuable information.

DEFINITION

A percentage is a part of a whole. It expresses one number as a portion of another.

$$\frac{\text{part}}{\text{whole}} = \text{percentage}$$

STEPS

It takes only four steps to figure out percentages: two questions and two operations.

1. "What is 100%, or the whole?" (Or, in some cases, "What is the starting point?")

2. What is the portion, or part, that you're interested in?

3. Divide the *portion* by the *whole*.

4. Move the decimal point two places to the right, and round, if necessary. (Percentages are expressed as portions of 100 rather than portions of 1, which is why we need to move the decimal point two places.)

KEY CONCEPT

Ordinary decimal numbers relate to 1, while percentages relate to 100. That's why we move the decimal point two places to the right to get a percentage.

$$\text{Decimal} \longrightarrow \begin{array}{c}\text{2 places to}\\\text{the right}\end{array} \longrightarrow \text{Percentage}$$

Let's use these steps to go back over the population figures, first in 1900 and then today:

In 1900, the whole, or total population in the U.S., was 76 million Americans. The part we're interested in is the 3 million over the age of 65.

The percentage is:

$$\frac{3 \text{ million}}{76 \text{ million}} = .039 = 3.9\%$$

Moving the decimal point two places to the right, we get 3.9%, and, after we round, 4%.

$$\text{Decimal} \longrightarrow \begin{array}{c}\text{2 places to}\\\text{the right}\end{array} \longrightarrow \text{Percentage}$$

$$.39 \longrightarrow .39 \longrightarrow 39\%$$

Doing the same for today's figures, we get:

$$\frac{32 \text{ million}}{263 \text{ million}} = .1216 = 12.16\%$$

Moving the decimal point two places to the right, we get 12.16%, which rounds to 12%.

Finally, we might want to ask what percentage increase this age group has seen over this period.

First, we determine how many more senior Americans there are now than before. If there were 3 million then and there are 32 million today, that's an increase in raw numbers of 29 million. The portion we want to compare is this increase of 29 million versus the starting number, 3 million:

$$\frac{29 \text{ million}}{3 \text{ million}} = 9.66 = 966\%$$

Moving the decimal two places to the right, we get 966%. We could even round up, saying it's an increase in older Americans of nearly 1000%.

As you can see, a percentage can be greater than 100%. Most of the percentages you're likely to deal with are less than 100%, but as this example shows, they can be over 100%.

What does 100% mean?

Investment Example

Let's look at an example. Say your investments earned a whopping 100% in one year, even though this is rather improbable. Let's say you started with $10,000 at the beginning of the year, and your investments earned 100% over the next twelve months. How much would you have at the end of the year? We'll leave taxes out of this question, for the moment. Just concentrate on the mathematical question: "what is 100% of $10,000?"

That's right, another $10,000. If the whole was $10,000, your starting amount, then earning 100% would mean you earned a whopping $10,000. Thus, you would have twice what you started with, or $20,000, at the end of the year. You would have doubled your money.

Continue this investment madness for another year. What if your investments *decreased* 50% during the next year. What would you have at the end of the second year, besides an ulcer?

Well, if you started with $20,000 at the beginning of the second year and decreased that amount by 50%, or half, then you would be back to your original $10,000. Since half of $20,000 is $10,000, you lost your entire first-year gain and ended up back where you started.

You'll notice that by increasing a quantity by 100% and then decreasing it by 50%, you return to your original amount. This might seem surprising. It would be easy to think that a 100% increase followed by a 50% decrease would leave you with a quantity

50% greater than your original amount. As you can see, however, that's not how it works. The lesson here is that you can't just add percentages in a cumulative way. This is because every percentage is connected to a specific original amount. When you're following an investment through multiple years of change, then each year the original amount is different. Percentages from different years cannot be combined directly.

To calculate an investment's changes over several years, you have to work out each year's increase or decrease separately. You could also use algebra, which will be dealt with in chapter 9.

Here's another investment question. If your investments increase by 50% this year and then decrease by 50% next year, how much will you have at the end of next year? Remember, you can't can't add or subtract percentages.

Let's say you have $50,000 and your investments increased by 50% during the year—another tremendous result. How much would you have at the end of the year? You'd have $75,000, because $50,000 plus $25,000 (50% of $50,000) equals $75,000. Now for the second year: if you were able to perform the same miracle in the opposite direction—that is, to incur a loss of 50%—how much would you have? You would lose one-half of $75,000, or $37,500, and you would end up with $37,500, the remaining half.

Here again you can see that percentages can't simply be added or subtracted. In this example, your investment increases by 50% and then decreases by 50%, and you end up with less than you started with. The increase and decrease were of different dollar amounts, because each year you started with a different amount of money. Since you had more money at the beginning of the second year, you lost more than you gained during the first year. One-half of $75,000 was more than one-half of $50,000. It's like the old saying: the bigger they are, the harder they fall.

PERCENTAGES ARE POWER

You might be starting to see the possibilities here. You can take almost any pair of numbers and calculate comparisons in the form of percentages. Many people use percentages for just this purpose. Some do it to sway or persuade others, rather than to present facts objectively. When you see any percentage, you should ask yourself, "what is the presenter or author really trying to say, and, most importantly, what is being left out?" After all, a percentage is just a mathematical calculation. It's the human calculation that we have to be wary of.

For instance, a broker tells you that he has increased your stock investment portfolio by a whopping 20% in 1997! That's good, right? Well, what if you knew that the stock market, the S&P 500 was up 23% and the Dow Jones 28% in 1997? How would you then feel about the broker's boast? Much less impressed. With percentages, especially in sales or other situations which require techniques of persuasion you have to ask yourself: what is being left out? Numbers taken out of context can be extremely misleading.

When giving a management presentation, you need to be careful about the numbers you use. You also need to anticipate the logical questions that you may have to field.

Know the source of your facts: Check and document your figures. For instance, the population figures used above were obtained from *The Sociological Almanac for the United States*, 1961, The Bedminister Press, New York, page 31, table 2; and "The Economics of Aging," *Business Week*, September 12, 1994, page 60; and the 1996 *Universal Almanac*, page 355.

Tax Example

Let's change the subject. At the top of the first page of this chapter, we talked about earning $35,000 and paying taxes of $8,500.

We asked this question: if you earned $35,000 and paid $8,500 in income taxes (including federal income taxes, social security FICA taxes, and state income taxes), what percentage is that? We only have to ask two questions and perform the two mathematical operations of division and moving the decimal point:

First, what is the whole, or 100%? It's your annual income, $35,000. That's what we're comparing the taxes to. Second, what is the part that we're interested in? It's the $8,500, the part of your salary that went toward taxes.

Third, we divide the part by the whole. That's $8,500 divided by $35,000, which equals .2428.

Fourth (and finally), we move the decimal point two places to the right to get 24.28%. After we round, we get 24%. In other words, about one-fourth (24% is close to 25%) of your income goes to taxes

Taxes we pay: Besides income taxes, we pay sales taxes and perhaps real estate taxes, if you own a house, condo or co-op.

Remember that what's being withheld from your paycheck may not be enough for your federal and state income taxes. The amount withheld from your paycheck is only an estimate. On April 15 of each year, we even up and find out who owes whom. Do you owe the government, or do they owe you (because too much or too little was withheld)?

As a rule, don't be too quick to change your withholding if you get a refund. Accountants will tell you that you shouldn't give a tax-free loan to the government. That's technically what you are doing if you get a refund.

However, accountants aren't experts in human nature. Sometimes people need to be clever to save money, and getting a refund for some people is one way. It's forced savings. It may pay for the vacation or whatever. I've known people who take the accountant's advice and end up frittering away the money and at April 15 have no refund either.

ROUNDING

What is rounding and why do we use it? *Rounding* means changing an exact number to a nearby number that's easier to read, like changing 3.129 to 3, or changing 149 to 150. We do it because it makes numbers easier to understand at a glance.

Rounding can put numbers into perspective for casual readers. The decision to round a number is a judgement call. Sometimes, precision is more important than ease of reading. If scientists were measuring the levels of deadly toxins in your tap water, for example, you'd probably want them to calculate their results quite precisely. When exact numbers are less crucial, however, rounded numbers are often preferable. If a contractor tells you at the end of the day that your house is 38.68% painted, for example, you're probably getting too much information. It's enough to know that the job is about 40% done.

In our tax example above, you learned that 24.28% of your income was paid in income taxes. The complexity of this number can make it difficult to get a clear perspective of how much you're paying. By rounding to the closest number and then rounding to the closest percentage, the numbers can be more meaningful. One-fourth of your income in taxes presents a more telling picture.

MOVING TWO DECIMALS POINTS TO THE RIGHT

Why do we move two to the right? After dividing as we did above and getting the answer .2428, why do we need to shift the decimal point? The answer is that it makes more sense to relate everything to

100%. *A decimal relates everything to 1, whereas a percentage relates everything to 100.* It's a matter of convention, and both decimals and percentages work. You should feel comfortable using both. What if you're given a percentage and need to change it back to a decimal? You guessed it: just move that decimal point two places to the left.

Tax Example

What is the difference between the marginal and effective tax rate? The marginal tax rate is the highest rate of your taxes, while the effective rate is your average rate. Here is the 1997 tax schedule:

Single Tax Rate Schedule For 1997

If taxable income is:	The tax rate is:
$0 up to $24,650:	15%
$24,650 up to $59,750:	$3,697.50 plus 28% over $24,650
$59,750 up to $124,650:	$13,525.50 plus 31% over $59,750
$124,650 up to $271,050:	$33,644.50 plus 36% over $124,650
$271,050 and over:	$86,348.50 plus 39.6% over $271,050

Married Tax Rate Schedule For 1997

If taxable income is:	The tax rate is:
$0 up to $41,200:	15%
$41,200 up to $99,600:	$6,180 plus 28% over $41,200
$99,600 up to $151,750:	$22,532 plus 31% over $99,600
$151,750 up to $271,050:	$38,698.50 plus 36% over $151,750
$271,050 and over:	$81,646.50 plus 39.6% over $271,050

As you can see, the tax schedule is organized in steps depending on total income. What you might not know is that very few people pay taxes at just one percentage rate. For example, a married couple making a combined $180,000 annually are said to be in the 36% tax bracket. That doesn't mean that they pay 36% of their income in taxes, though. In fact, they pay 15% of their income up to $41,200; 28% of their income after that up to $99,600; then 31% of their income after that up to $151,750, and finally 36% on their income thereafter up to $180,000, their total income. The highest percentage they pay is 36% (that's their marginal rate), but the total amount of taxes they pay will be less than 36% of their total income. The percentage of their income paid in taxes when all's said and done is their effective rate.

Let's say you're married and you and your spouse earn $65,000. You don't take itemized deductions, and you have no kids, yet. To calculate your federal taxable income given these numbers, subtract the standard deduction of $6,900 for a married couple (the standard deduction is $4,150 for singles) and two exemptions of $2,650 each. These are freebies for everyone, and they give you and your spouse a total deduction of $12,200.

Then, subtract $12,200 from $65,000 to obtain your taxable income (this first $12,200 is not taxed at all). Your taxable income is therefore $52,800.

Examining the tax schedule, we can see that you'll be in the 28% federal tax bracket. In the real world, you'd also have state taxes to pay, but let's concentrate for now on the federal. To calculate your federal taxes from the schedule, we'll do one long string of calculations. Get your pocket calculator and follow along:

- enter 52800 (taxable income)

- minus 41200 (beginning of 28% bracket)

- equals (you should have 11600 showing)

- times .28 (the 28% bracket in decimal form)

- equals (you should have 3248 showing)

- plus 6180 (the tax of the first $41,200)

- equals 9428

That's your federal tax, $9,428. You could have done separate calculations, but this string of calculations is handy once you get the hang of it.

Your marginal tax bracket is 28% in this case. This is used to calculate any taxes with an increase in income, as long as it's still within the 28% bracket.

Your effective tax rate is simply your taxes divided by your total income:

$$\frac{\$9,428}{\$65,000} = .145$$

In this case it's 14.5%, or about 15%. That is, your average tax rate is about 15% of your total income. You get to keep 85%.

COMMON PERCENTAGES

Here are some percentages you meet frequently and their fractional equivalents.

10% is one-tenth

25% is one-fourth

33% is one-third

50% is one-half

67% is two-thirds

75% is three-fourths

90% is nine-tenths

Tipping Example

Let's have more fun than taxes; let's go eat.

Paying the check is a familiar after-meal chore. And although tips are not customary in some countries, like Japan, and in others it's mostly added to the bill, as in Europe, here in America, land of liberty, we enjoy the freedom to do difficult math ourselves. It's not really optional, though. Out waiters and waitresses would be rather irate if we didn't leave a tip. (I was once told that the word tip stands for *To Insure Prompt* service)

The general rule, as we all know, is to add 15% to the total. The only problem is that you usually don't take a calculator to the restaurant. Or so you think. Actually, you do have a calculator—your brain, the fabulous human calculator. There are two simple methods for figuring tips.

Method One: Calculate 10% and then add one-half more. That gets you to 15%. Then you can add or subtract from that point depending on how the food was and how attentive the waiter or waitress was, or was not. Calculating 10% just means moving the decimal point one place to the left. If the bill is $30, then 10% is $3. One-half of $3 is $1.50. Add them both and you get $4.50, or 15%.

Method Two: Calculate 20% and round down. First calculate 10%, then double to get 20%. If the bill is $40, 10% is $4, double that to get $8. Then round down to, say, $6.

You can, of course, do it both ways. Since you start with 10% in either method, doing it both ways can keep your tip in the right ballpark, and prove to your guests that you can do this as easily as carrying on a conversation.

In New York, since the tax is about 8%, we can double the tax and get about 15%!

Unfortunately, the totals never seem to be even numbers. More likely the total is something like $45.36. First, we'll forget the cents, and thus we consider only the $45.

Quick, what is 10% of $45? It's $4.50. What is one half of $4.50? This may not be so easy. You could see that if the original number was $4.00, then one-half would be $2. To do this quickly and roughly, we can simply add $2 to the $4.50 to get $6.50, and then round up to, say, $7. If you didn't like the service or meal, you could be a little stingy by only giving $6, or even $4.50, a meager 10%.

You could also use the 20% method. 10% of $45 is $4.50. Doubling gives us $9. Rounding down gives us about $7,or so. The key to this is starting with 10% and rounding.

RULE

Fractions, decimals, and percentages are all related.

SALE—THIS SATURDAY ONLY!

Stores *mark up* and *mark down* prices as it suits them, to attract customers and make a profit.

Markup Example

A typical store buys a sports coat from a wholesaler for, say, $30. The store, the retailer, marks it up, say, 50%, a common percentage. As a result, the price of the sports coat for you and me is $45. We arrived at this by first multiplying the $30 by .50 (yes, we converted back to decimals for calculations). Multiplying $30 by .50 gives you $15. That's the markup, making the sports coat a retail price of $45 ($30 + $15 = $45).

Markdown Example

You like the coat, but are waiting for it to go on sale. Let's say you're lucky and it goes on sale for 10% off. That is, it will be 10% lower in price than $45. How much will it be reduced? Multiply $45 by .10 (that's 10% converted to decimals) to get $4.50. The sale price is therefore $40.50 ($45 – $4.50 = $40.50). The retailer may even play psychologist and put it on sale for $39—a common tactic to make goods more attractive. We seem to be suckers for $29, $39, $49, and so forth.

You could also calculate 10% off in a more direct way. We could multiply the current price of $45 by 90%. Since you are going to pay 10% less than 100%, your price will be 90% of the original cost. You can get your price by multiplying the original price by .90:

$$\$45 \times .90 = \$40.50$$

USING CALCULATORS TO FIND PERCENTAGES

Although we'll save our pointers about calculators for a later chapter, little hand-held calculators are everywhere and it is assumed that you used them as you went through the numbers in this chapter. You did follow along doing the calculations didn't you?

Many of these simple calculators have a % key. Get one in front of you and let's do this last calculation using it. Enter 45 (for 45 dollars) press the × key (for multiplying) then enter 90 and press the % key. Your answer should say 40.50. Most, but not all, calculators that have the % key work this way.

You can also use the % key for the markup problem. Enter 30 (for $30), press the × key, enter 50 and press the % key. It should show 15, for $15. Add $15 to $30 for the retail marked up price of $45.

To get this last answer directly, you can multiply by 1.50 and do both steps in one. Enter 30 (for $30), press the x key, enter 1.50 and press the % key. Presto, you've gotten $45. The one stands for 100% and the .50 stands for the markup percentage of 50%. Together they make 150%, or in decimal form, 1.50, or simply 1.5.

FINAL CAUTION

We've reviewed the basics and several examples of percentages. Percentages are everywhere, and they have the ring of authority. The main caution to remember is a general caution with numbers: don't be intimidated by mathematics. We have to be careful not to stop thinking once we're faced with a percentage or any other number. In fact, we have to *start* thinking when we see numbers of any kind. We should start asking questions. Where did you get that number? Is that number valid? Are there more important numbers to consider? And so forth.

QUIZ

Question 1: Suppose your total investments were $50,000 and of that total, you had allocated $15,000 to a S&P 500 fund, $5,000 to a small cap fund, $7,000 to an international fund, $18,000 to an intermediate bond fund, and $5,000 to a money market fund. If the S&P 500 fund, the small cap fund, and the international fund all represent stock-market investments, what is the percentage of your total investments allocated to the stock market?

Answer 1: 54%. You first need to determine what categories would be considered invested in the stock market. There are three in this case: the $15,000 in the S&P 500, $5,000 in a small cap fund, and $7,000 in an international fund. Together they total $27,000. So, $27,000 is what percent of your total investment?

$$\frac{\$27,000}{\$50,000} = .54$$

Moving the decimal point two places to the right, you get the percentage: 54%

Question 2: If you had $84,000 in investments at the beginning of the year and increased it to $93,000 by the end of the year, then you have increased your investments by what percent?

Answer 2: 10.7%. First, determine how much money in dollars your investments made: $93,000 minus $84,000 equals $9,000. That is, your investments grew $9,000 from a starting amount of $84,000. To determine the percent:

$$\frac{\$9,000}{\$84,000} = .107$$

Moving the decimal point places to the right, you get the percentage: 10.7

SUMMARY

PURPOSE

Percentages add meaning to numbers. They show differences and comparisons that raw numbers can't.

DEFINITION

A percentage is a part of a whole. It expresses a number as a portion of another number.

STEPS

It takes only four steps to figure out a percentages: two questions and two operations.

1. "What is 100%, or the whole?" (Or, in some cases, "What is the starting point?")

2. What is the portion, or part, that you're interested in?

3. Divide the *portion* by the *whole.*

4. Move the decimal point two places to the right, and round, if necessary. (Percentages are expressed as portions of 100 rather than portions of 1, which is why we need to move the decimal point two places.)

KEY CONCEPT

Ordinary decimal numbers relate to 1, while percentages relate to 100. That's why we move the decimal point two places to the right to get a percentage.

CAUTION

Check and document your figures and anticipate questions you'll be asked.

APPLICATIONS

Population, investments, taxes, markup and markdown and tipping.

2

Conversions

If the U.S. dollar is strong relative to the yen, it benefits American tourists who travel to Japan. On the other hand, it hurts U.S. manufacturers trying to export to Japan.

Do you follow this logic?

Mental gymnastics of this kind are unfamiliar to most people. Although we reluctantly convert inches to feet or quarts to liters from time to time, nothing seems as complicated as converting one currency to another. When traveling in Europe, one often visits several countries. In a short span of time, you may need to do business in francs, liras, and deutsche marks.

After World War II, fixed exchange rates between countries were established by the Bretton Woods conference. Under fixed exchange rates, currencies cannot change in value with respect to one another; these fixed arrangements caused some strange distortions in the marketplace, however, because the currencies of different economies naturally tend to fluctuate in value. The fixed-rate arrangement lasted until 1973, when the U.S. went to a floating rate of exchange with other countries, allowing the dollar to change in value with respect to other currencies. Until 1971 the U.S. also maintained a gold standard, which meant that the value of the dollar was linked to the price of gold, and dollars could be exchanged freely for gold at that rate. Fixed rates and convertibility to gold gave us an orderly, stable financial world. Now, with a dollar whose value isn't linked to any other commodity, the financial world can seem like a floating crap game.

PURPOSE

Why do we have to convert currencies, anyway? Because we live in a global village! Modern economic activity takes place across all national borders. Multinational companies do business in different currencies simultaneously, according to the location of their offices and markets. Changes in exchange rates can have a dramatic impact on such companies. As long as the world divides its markets with many different currencies, exchange-rate issues will be with us. Currently, many of the nations of Europe are negotiating to give up their individual currencies in favor of a common currency, the *euro* but it's a difficult road for them, and it's not clear yet whether France, Germany and Italy will actually give up their colorful currencies. There are strong forces of nationalist sentiment involved, and for many it's hard to imagine traveling in Europe without this variety of exotic-looking paper money and coins.

In 1790, as our country was just getting started, the Founding Fathers were faced with a related problem, a situation unthinkable today: different states issuing their own currencies. George Washington had to deal with state currencies and foreign currencies, all commonly used in our fledgling country. The Constitution then secured the sole right to coin money to the federal government. Alexander Hamilton created the First Bank of the United States, we have done business in a single currency ever since.

Globally, however, the economic tower of babel continues. Because we're stuck, for the foreseeable future, with so many currencies (over 200 around the world), it's impossible to understand finance and economics without understanding the impact of these different currencies and their exchange rates.

Economics Example

Consider the following two stories printed on November 22, 1996 in the business section of the *New York Times:*

> The British pound reached another four-year high against the dollar yesterday, driven by evidence of economic health in Britain that is expected to lead to higher interest rates.

Toyota Motor Corp., which has turned its exporting engine on full-blast in recent months amid robust U.S. orders and a strong U.S. dollar... Officials of the Big Three U.S. auto makers are griping that the dollar's new strength makes their exports less competitive overseas.

We notice that this currency business deeply affects businesses and economies. We also note that currencies move differently with respect to other currencies. The pound is getting stronger against the dollar, the dollar is getting stronger against the yen, and thereby, the pound was also getting much stronger against the yen.

DEFINITION

A conversion is a relationship between two things.

Fahrenheit to centigrade, pounds to dollars, miles to meters or inches to feet.

STEPS

There are only a few things to remember about conversions:

1. One item A will buy how many of item B? One dollar will buy 1,500 lira.

2. One item B will buy how many of item A? Just the opposite relationship. One lira will buy .0006682 dollars (.0006682 is 1/1500).

3. Can we use a simple calculator or formula to ease our conversion calculations?

Let's use these steps as we go traveling to Italy, one of my favorite destinations. In Italy in 1989, one dollar bought me 1,410 lira– cost of a bottle of Coke, which came in handy during the hot summer days in Florence.

In 1989: 1 dollar equaled 1,410 lira

In 1996: 1 dollar equaled 1,500 lira

QUESTION

In 1996, it takes more lira than it did in 1989 to buy a given number of dollars. Does this make the dollar stronger or weaker?

It makes the dollar *stronger* because one dollar can buy more lira. The lira became weaker against the dollar. For American tourists, this is good news. Our dollar can buy more lira, which means more cokes, which means we can travel more cheaply.

For the natives of the Ponte Vecchio, however, this change in the exchange rate could be expressed this way:

In   1989: 1 lira equaled .0007080 dollars

In   1996: 1 lira equaled .0006682 dollars

RULE

If you're a traveler, you want your own country's currency to be stronger with respect to the currencies of the countries you're visiting
Let's use a simple diagram to show this:

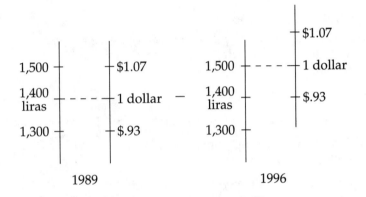

1989   1996

USING CALCULATORS WHEN TRAVELING TO FRANCE

Let's use a simple hand-held calculator with a memory. Let's say you're going to France and know the conversion factor between francs and dollars to be about 5.22 francs to 1 dollar, or about .19 dollars to one franc (about 20¢). Although this rate will fluctuate a penny or so (or several centimes) each day, at least in general you can keep your sense of how much things are costing you.

On your small calculator, enter one franc's value in dollars—in this case, .19—and then press the M+ key. You've now stored this number in your calculator's memory. Later, let's say you're sashaying along the Seine looking at art prints in the many small individual stalls. One catches your eye, and you see that it's priced at 85 francs. Because that doesn't tell you much as an American, you need to convert the price back to dollars, where you have a better sense of how much things cost. Out comes your calculator. On many calculators, even after the calculator is turned off, the memory stays intact. If that's not true of your calculator, you'll just have to jot the exchange rate down:

- enter 85 (for francs)

- press the × key (for multiplying)

- press the MR (memory recall) key, or your calculator's equivalent, which automatically brings up the .19. Alternatively, enter the exchange rate you jotted down.

- press the = key to get your result, $16.15

You say to yourself that $16.00 seems like a reasonable price for the print, and you hand over your francs.

To clear memory as you move onto Britain or Italy, just press the MR key twice. This usually clears the memory, and the little M disappears from the window.

KEY ECONOMIC CONCEPTS

Why do currencies get stronger or weaker? Let's come back to our news articles from the *New York Times*, where the stronger British pound and higher interest rates were related, and where a stronger dollar is causing problems for Detroit.

Currencies get stronger or weaker for a number of reasons, but here are some common causes:

1. If a country, like Britain, has higher interest rates, investors around the world will try to put money into British investments to get the higher returns. To do so, they will need to trade in their currencies for pounds, thus increasing the demand for the pound and bidding up its price, making it stronger relative to other currencies.

2. If a country, like Japan, wants a weaker currency to stimulate sales to the U.S., their central bank can sell yen and buy dollars, thus driving up the price of dollars versus yen. Japanese manufacturers can then increase their sales and profits with increased sales to the U.S.

Thus, pounds are stronger than dollars, and dollars are stronger than yen, at least for the moment. These things change over time. A confluence of several economic and financial forces can drive the dollar up or down relative to other currencies. Such factors include cheaper labor, lower inflation, and a more stable economy.

RULE

If you are an American exporter, you want a weak dollar; if you're an American importer, you want a strong dollar.

Thus, the dilemma for Britain, Japan, and Detroit, and indeed everyone who does business across national borders, is that these economic and trade issues are closely tied to currency movements, and thereby consumers at home and tourists abroad are directly affected. Exchange rates affect everyone.

KEY INVESTMENT CONCEPT

If you are invested in international mutual funds, you'll do better if the dollar is weaker, because it increases the returns you obtain. All dividends, interest, and capital gains produce greater payoffs in dollars when the dollar is weak relative to foreign currencies. In an international fund, where many currencies may be represented, the dollar should be weak relative to all the currencies invested in the fund, not just one or two.

RULE

If you are an American international investor, you want a weaker dollar.

FARENHEIT TO CENTRIGRADE (CELSIUS) AND BACK

Yes, we declared our independence from Britain and adopted the decimal system for our money, but we kept the old Standard measurement system for practically everything else. Today, we're stuck with these old units, even though we've made attempts to convert to centigrade and the metric system. Perhaps in time, the U.S. will fall into step with the rest of the world.

For now, picture yourself in sunny Provence, France enjoying yourself in Paul Cézanne country. The local paper says the temperature is a wintry 19°, but it feels fine. That's because the reading in the paper is given on the centigrade, or Celsius, scale. The temperature is actually what an American would call 66.2° Fahrenheit. There is a method for converting centigrade temperatures to Fahrenheit, but before we give you that formula, here's a shortcut that gets you close in a hurry.

SHORTCUT RULE

Centigrade to Fahrenheit—round, multiply by two, and add 30

Thus, if they say 19°, round to 20, multiply by two to get 40, and add 30 to get 70° Fahrenheit. That's within a few degrees of being 66.2°, which is respectably accurate.

That's a lot easier than the formula we learned in school but promptly forgot:

$$\frac{9}{5} \times \underline{C} + 32 = \underline{F}$$

or the opposite formula:

$$(\underline{F} - 32) \times \frac{5}{9} = \underline{C}$$

SHORTCUT RULE

> *Fahrenheit to centigrade* — round, subtract 30, and divide by two.

So tell your visitors from overseas this simple conversion. If we say 69° fahrenheit, round to 70, subtract 30 to get 40, divide by 2 to get 20° centigrade. That's surely close enough to their precise 20.5° centigrade.

TOOLING ALONG THE AUTOBAHN

I was doing 105 on the German superhighway and my daughter seemed concerned. "Dad," she asked nervously, "why are you driving so fast?" I had to explain that 105 k.p.h. (kilometers per hour) was only about 65 m.p.h.—an unremarkable highway speed in the States. After a big Mercedes passed us like we were standing still, she seemed less concerned.

The formula for mile/kilometer conversion is:

- If you know kilometers, multiply by .62 to get miles. For example, if you're traveling at 105 k.p.h., that's equivalent to 65 m.p.h. (105 × .62 = 65.1).

- If you know miles, multiply by 1.61 to get kilometers. For example, if you're traveling at 65 m.p.h., that's the same as 105 k.p.h. (65 × 1.61 = 104.65).

SHORTCUT RULE

Multiply the kilometer speedometer by .6. Thus, if you're going 100 k.p.h. on the Autobahn or Autostrada, your speed is roughly equal to 60 m.p.h. back home.

COMMON MEASUREMENT CONVERSIONS
Length:

one inch	.083 feet	2.540 centimeters
one foot	12 inches	.305 meters
one yard	3 feet	.914 meters
one rod	16.5 feet	5.029 meters
one mile	5,280 feet	1.609 meters
one nautical mile	1.151 statute mile	1.852 kilometers
one centimeter	4.68 feet	.39 inches
one meter	3.28 feet	39.36 inches
one kilometer	.62 miles	3,273 feet

Area:

one square inch	.007 square foot	6.452 square centimeters
one square foot	144 square inches	929 square meters
one square yard	9 square feet	.836 square meter
one acre	43,560 square feet	4.047 square meters
one square mile	640 acres	2.59 square meters

Volume:

one cubic inch	.00058 cubic foot	16.387 cubic centimeters
one cubic foot	1.728 cubic inches	.028 cubic meter
one cubic yard	27 cubic feet	.765 cubic meter

Miscellaneous:

4 pecks	1 bushel
one ounce	16 drams
one dram	60 grams
one carat	3.086 grams or 200 milligrams
one pennyweight	24 grams
one pound	16 ounces
one ton	2,000 pounds
speed of sound	1,088 feet per second
speed of light	186,000 miles per second or 300,000 kilometers per second

IF YOU DON'T HAVE A RULER

- the diameter of a quarter is about one inch

- business cards are 2 inches by $3\frac{1}{2}$ inches

- dollar bills, like all American bills, are 6 inches by almost 3 inches

- a sheet of typing paper is $8\frac{1}{2}$ inches by 11 inches

QUIZ

Question 1: If French francs could buy more dollars, is this the time for you to travel to France or should you wait?

Question 2: If you invested in an international stock fund, would you want the dollar to be strong or weak against other currencies?

Answer 1: No, wait until the dollar is stronger. Unless it's your honeymoon, in which case you ought to go anyway.

Answer 2: Weak. If the dollar is weak, international returns will be greater when converted to dollars.

SUMMARY

PURPOSE

We have to convert because we live in a global village, in which business is done in multiple currencies. Americans must do extra conversion, because we don't use the same measurement system as the rest of the world.

DEFINITION

A conversion changes the expression of a quantity from one set of units into another, without changing the quantity itself. Different units can have a fixed relationship.

STEPS

There are only a few things to remember about conversions:

1. One item A will buy how many of item B? For example, one dollar will buy 1,500 lira.

2. One item B will buy how many of item A? Just the opposite relationship: one lira will buy .0006682 dollars (.0006682 is 1/1500).

3. Can we use a simple calculator or formula to ease our conversion calculations?

RULES

- If you're a traveler, you want your currency to be stronger than the currency of the country you're visiting.

- If you're an American exporter, you want a weak dollar; if you're an American importer, you want a strong dollar.

- If you're an American international investor, you want a weak dollar.

SHORTCUT

1. Centigrade to Fahrenheit, round, multiply by two and add 30.

2. Multiply the kilometer speedometer by .6 to get m.p.h.

KEY ECONOMIC CONCEPTS

- If a country, like Britain, has higher interest rates, investors around the world will try to put money into British investments to get the higher returns. To do so, they will need to trade in their currencies for pounds, thus increasing the demand for the pound and bidding up its price, making it stronger relative to other currencies.

- If a country, like Japan, wants a weaker currency to stimulate sales to the U.S., their central bank can sell yen and buy dollars, thus driving up the price of dollars versus yen. Japanese manufacturers can then increase their sales and profits with increased sales to the U.S.

APPLICATIONS

Currencies, finance, economics, temperature, and measurements of all kinds.

Ratios

A company's price-to-earnings ratio or P/E ratio compares the price of one share of that company's stock to the amount of money that each share will earn in one year. If the P/E ratio of a company is low (meaning that its price is low compared to its yearly earnings), some investors consider that company's stock a bargain that should be bought. Other investors, who believe that the market finds the right price, say that only companies with high P/E ratios should be bought, because those are the stocks that the stock market considers good values.

Two sides of the same coin?

In investing, there are rules, and then there are rules. Investors who favor buying stocks with low P/E ratios are called *value* investors. They believe that stocks whose prices are low relative to their earnings are often underpriced, and likely to increase in value over time. Such stocks would therefore be good long-term investments.

On the other hand, another group of investors, called *growth* investors, say that only those stocks with higher-than-average P/E ratios should be bought. These investors believe that high-priced stocks cost more than other stocks because the stock market believes that they'll grow in value. Indeed, the widespread belief that a company's stock is valuable often causes its price to rise independently of what the company is doing. Growth investors believe that the stock market does a good job of pricing stocks wisely, meaning that low-priced stocks are cheap for a reason (they're not great stocks), and high-priced stocks are expensive because they're likely to be the best investments in the long run.

The terms "value" and "growth" are somewhat deceptive, because, after all, every investor wants both. Different people define them differently.

Before we spend any more time on the value versus growth debate, let's first look at what a ratio is and, specifically, what this P/E ratio is all about, and why it appears in almost all stock quotations.

PURPOSE

Why do we use *ratios*? *Because they show how one thing is related to another*. Prices versus earnings, current assets versus current liabilities, dividends versus earnings, sales versus inventory, and profits versus sales, are just a few of the ratios used in business. They allow us to analyze a company.

KEY CONCEPT

Ratios can be written various ways. Ratios are fractions, and are often written as such:

$$\frac{price}{earnings}$$

A ratio of two numbers is the result obtained by dividing one of the numbers by the other. A *P/E ratio*, specifically, is the price of a stock divided by its yearly earnings per share. If you saw that a stock had a P/E ratio of 18.0, then you'd know that the stock's price divided by its earnings per share is 18.0. In other words, the price of a share is 18 times what that share will earn in a year.

In more formal math, a ratio can also be written with a colon between the two quantities:

$$P:E$$

When a ratio is written in this form, the number that would go on top of the fraction comes first. All of these written forms have the same meaning, and express a between two quantities.

DEFINITION

A ratio is one quantity divided by another, a fraction. A useful ratio allows us to see a relationship that is helpful in the analysis of a company, industry, or the economy as a whole.

In a P/E ratio, a fundamental relationship is exposed: the price of a company's stock is related to the earnings per share of common stock. It's considered by investors as the mother of all ratios, and is usually listed next to the daily price of stocks in the *Wall Street Journal*, as well as in your local newspaper. It summarizes in one place the two critical aspects of a company: what people are willing to pay for it (price) and how much money it's making (earnings).

Notice, by the way, that a P/E ratio doesn't tell you what a stock's price and earnings *are*; it just tells you how they're related. A stock with a P/E ratio of 18.0, for example, could have a price of $18.00 per share and annual earnings of $1.00 per share; or it could have a price of $180.00 per share and annual earnings of $10.00 per share. All the ratio tells you is that the price is 18 times annual earnings.

If the price increases faster than earnings, resulting in an increasing P/E ratio, investors are anticipating the company's earnings to be good in the future. If the price of a stock is not increasing as fast as its earnings, resulting in a decreasing P/E ratio, that means that investors have decided that the earnings are probably not sustainable.

P/E Example

Let's look at two well known companies at different points in time, as reported in *Barron's*, a weekly publication for serious investors:

Week ending January 4, 1993:

	volume	div	P/E	high	low	end	chg
Exxon	60351	2.88	17	$66\frac{1}{2}$	$65\frac{1}{2}$	$66\frac{1}{2}$	$+\frac{1}{2}$
Microsoft	102956	...	26	$84\frac{1}{2}$	$80\frac{1}{2}$	82	+2

Week ending January 3, 1997:

	volume	div	P/E	high	low	end	chg
Exxon	66944	3.16	18	101	$96\frac{1}{2}$	$98\frac{5}{8}$	$+1\frac{1}{4}$
Microsoft	200246	...	47	$85\frac{5}{8}$	$80\frac{3}{4}$	$84\frac{5}{8}$	$+\frac{3}{8}$

Exxon is a mature company, while Microsoft is a relatively new and dynamic one. Both are popularly traded, Exxon on the New York Stock Exchange and Microsoft on the over-the-counter exchange called the NASDAQ exchange. Early in December 1996, Microsoft reached around 160 and split two for one. The volume is in hundreds, so the number of Exxon stock trades in the week shown in 1993 is running over 6 million (60351 plus two 0s for 100 equals 6,035,100) while Microsoft had over 10 million stock trades in that week. The week shown in 1997 saw over 6 million trades for Exxon and 20 million for Microsoft. *Barron's*, being a weekly publication, gives weekly figures. You could divide by 5 and get the average volume per day.

Exxon pays a dividend (abbreviated "div" in the tables) that slowly increased from $2.88 per year in 1993 to $3.16 per year more currently. A dividend is a periodic payment by which a company distributes a portion of its profits to its shareholders. Microsoft pays no dividends, which is typical for a young company. They want to use their earnings for internal purposes such as hiring more people, expanding their offices, buying new computers, and so on.

These two P/E ratios are instructive. Historically, the average P/E ratio for all companies is around 15, so Exxon is about average. Investors have estimated that Exxon will grow steadily, but not spectacularly. Microsoft's P/E ratio went from 26 to 47 in the three years between our glimpses—from high to very high. Investors are estimating that Microsoft will continue to grow in an above-average way for the foreseeable future.

By the way, if you wanted to verify the calculation of the P/E ratio yourself, you could easily find the price of the stock in any stock table. But to look up the company's earnings, which in this case means earnings-per-share of common stock, you would need to consult the income statement in the company's annual report for the total earnings. Then, from the balance sheet in the annual report, you could learn the number of outstanding shares of stock. Divide the total earnings (after first subtracting the earnings of preferred stock owners, if any) by the total number of stock to get the earnings-per-share. Finally, you could divide the price of the stock by this earnings-per-share figure to get the P/E ratio.

KEY CONCEPT

If you don't have a company's annual report, you can determine its earnings-per-share from what we already know. We know the P/E ratio and the price. All we have to do is move the formula around to find the earnings-per-share. We'll show this in more detail in the chapter on algebra, but here's a quick look for now:

$$\frac{\text{price}}{\text{P/E}} = \text{earnings per share}$$

This way, we can figure out the earnings-per-share for Microsoft in the two weeks we're looking at. On January 4, 1993, Microsoft's common stock share price was $82 and its P/E ratio was 26. Putting those numbers into our formula and solving, we obtain the figure of $3.15 for the earnings per share:

$$\frac{\$82}{26} = \$3.15$$

Using the price of $1.60 before it split, we get a slightly higher figure for the earnings per share, $3.40. That's an 8% increase:

$$\frac{\$160}{47} = \$3.40$$

In other words, the higher price and higher P/E ratio is simply keeping up with an increase of earnings per share.

By the way, cyclical stocks, like those of airlines and paper companies, to mention just two, tend to fluctuate according to the general business cycle—that is, grow when the economy is growing and slow down when business slows down. The P/E ratios of these cyclical stocks reflect this business cycle moving up and down naturally.

KEY CONCEPT

A ratio can increase or decrease as a result of the movement of one or both of the involved quantities.

Let's count the ways a ratio can *increase*:

1. If the top number increases while the bottom number stays relatively stable, the ratio increases.

2. If the bottom number decreases while the top number stays relatively stable, the ratio increases.

3. If both numbers increase but the price increases more, the ratio increases.

4. If both numbers decrease but the prices decrease less, the ratio increases.

Let's see this in action with Microsoft. First, we've already determined the earnings per share to be about $3.40 currently. Let's say, before the stock split, investors begin to feel even more positive about Microsoft and buy more of it, increasing its price.

Let's say the price is driven up quickly to $170, just to pick a number. What is the new P/E ratio?

$$\text{P/E of 500.} \quad \frac{\$170}{3.4} = 50$$

We'll let you play around with the other possibilities, but you get the idea. Either number can cause the P/E ratio to increase. To determine the ways a ratio can *decrease*, well, just reverse everything we said.

Ratios can be calculated for a company at one point in time, which is technically called *cross-sectional analysis*. Ratios can also be collected for a number of years to study trends, which is called *time-series analysis*. Cross-sectional analysis is like a geologist looking at a single strata of rock across the landscape. It's a financial analyst's way of looking at key relationships within a company or industry at one point in time. Time-series analysis is the attempt to discover trends in the development of a company or industry by tracking changes in various factors over time.

KEY CONCEPT

No one ratio tells a researcher enough to understand a company completely. Numerous ratios are often employed by professional analysts. Ratios are the backbone of what is called *fundamental analysis*, one of two ways investors, businesses, and creditors analyze companies. It involves analyzing pieces of the balance sheet and income statement, the two basic financial documents of a company. The other approach is called *technical analysis*, and involves charts and graphs of market volume and price movements.

Fundamental analysis can be further broken down into the study of different aspects of company operations: activity, liquidity, profitability, and P/E and other ratios. Analyzing changes in these ratios for a given company can give clues to the company's future success. By comparing the ratios of one company versus others in the same field, such as Mobil to Exxon, analysts find clues to the likelihood of success or failure for various companies.

Activity ratios measure the rate at which a company turns its inventory into cash. There are several sorts of activity ratios:

$$\frac{\text{sales}}{\text{average inventory}} = \text{inventory turnover}$$

$$\frac{\text{receivables}}{\text{sales per day}} = \text{average collection period}$$

$$\frac{\text{annual sales}}{\text{accounts receivable}} = \text{receivable turnover}$$

Liquidity ratios measure the ease of converting assets to cash, in case it's needed. There are two common ratios used:

$$\frac{\text{current assets}}{\text{current liabilities}} = \text{current ratio}$$

$$\frac{\text{current assets minus inventories}}{\text{current liabilities}} = \text{acid test}$$

The acid test is also known as the quick ratio.

Profitability ratios measure the earnings relative to sales, assets, or equity:

$$\frac{\text{earnings after taxes}}{\text{sales}} = \text{net profit margin}$$

$$\frac{\text{earnings after taxes}}{\text{total assets}} = \text{return on assets}$$

$$\frac{\text{earnings after taxes}}{\text{equity}} = \text{return on equity}$$

P/E and other ratios, including our P/E ratio:

$$\frac{\text{price}}{\text{earnings per share}} = \text{price earning ratio}$$

$$\frac{\text{debt}}{\text{equity}} = \text{debt ratio}$$

$$\frac{\text{dividends}}{\text{earnings}} = \text{payout ratio}$$

$$\frac{\text{earnings after taxes} - \text{preferred dividends}}{\text{equity} - \text{preferred stock}} = \text{return on equity}$$

Because there's a multitude of ratios that can calculated, you must decide which ratios are meaningful for your purpose when you do financial research. While investors rely on profitability and P/E ratios, bankers and other creditors look to the ability of a company to meet its short- and long-term financial obligations.

CAUTION

It's not uncommon for two professional analysts to look at a ratio and reach two nearly opposite conclusions based on it. Understanding the issues is necessary to understanding such differences in interpretation. To see what can be involved, let's finally return to the argument about value and growth investors with which this chapter began.

Value investors want to find companies that are undervalued—companies, that is, with lower-than-average P/E ratios. But will these companies truly grow faster than companies with higher P/E ratios? If these companies are really so cheap, why are they undervalued? Perhaps, some will say, they are valued properly after all, and will not grow quickly in the future. A simple question leaps to mind: historically, have all, or even most, "undervalued" companies grown faster than the stock market as a whole? The answer is, unfortunately, no. A low P/E ratio may provide a clue to a good investment, but it doesn't automatically indicate a good buy.

On the other hand, will all growth stocks (those with higher than average P/E ratios) continue to grow? Obviously not. By carefully tracking other ratios, the products the companies offer, the management teams in place in these companies and the overall business climate, researchers are able to offer more complete analysis of the growth potential of stocks.

USING CALCULATORS TO FIND RATIOS

Although we will save all of our pointers for using calculators for a later chapter, calculators are everywhere and it is assumed that you used them as you went through the ratios in this chapter. Many of these calculators have memory keys. These come in handy when we need to perform several calculations as we do in the acid test, or quick ratio, as it is sometimes called. You remember the formula:

$$\frac{\text{equity after taxes} - \text{preferred dividends}}{\text{equity} - \text{preferred stock}} = \text{return on equity}$$

The top number, or numerator, involves a subtraction. We can either perform each part of the ratio separately, or we can do a continuous calculation. We'll assume the following figures for the ratio:

- earnings after taxes are $450,000

- preferred stock dividends are $125,000

- equity is $2.7 million

- preferred stock is $125,000 ($1 par value)

Get your calculator with the memory and follow along:

- enter 2700000 (for $2.7 million equity—note we are starting with the denominator)

- minus 125000 (for $125,000 preferred stock)

- equals (you should have 2,575,000 showing)

- press the M+ key (an M should now show along with

the number, indicating that it's stored in the memory)

- enter 450000 (for earnings after taxes)
- minus 125000 (for preferred stock dividends)
- equals (you should have 325,000 showing)
- press the divide key
- press the MR key (this recalls the previously stored amount of 2,575,000)
- equals .126, or 12.6%

That's a return of 12.6% on equity, a reasonable amount. You could have done separate calculations, but this string of calculations using the calculator's memory is quite handy once you're familiar with it.

QUIZ

Question 1: What is a stock's P/E ratio if the price of a stock is $31.50, the company's total earnings are $1.26 million, and there are 600,000 shares outstanding?

Question 2: If the inventory turnover ratio of one company was 8.2 and that of a second company was 10.7, which company was more successful in selling their products? Assume both companies are in the same business.

Answer 1: 15. You first find the earnings per share: 1,260,000 divided by 600,000, or 2.1. If your calculator has a memory, you can store this result. Next, enter 31.50 for the price of the stock and divide by 2.1 to obtain the result of 15.

Answer 2: The second company. The second company's inventory turnover means that it turns over, or sells, its inventory 10.7 times a year, versus a slower 8.2 times for the first company.

It could also mean that the second company kept less inventory on hand, thus using a more sophisticated inventory system.

SUMMARY

PURPOSE

We use ratios because they show how one thing is related to another. Common ratios deal with prices versus earnings, current assets versus current liabilities, dividends versus earnings, sales versus inventory, and profits versus sales. They allow us to analyze the development of a company or industry.

DEFINITION

A ratio is one quantity divided by another, a fraction. A useful ratio allows us to see a relationship that is helpful in the analysis of a company, industry, or the economy as a whole.

KEY CONCEPT

Ratios can be written in various ways. Ratios are fractions, and are often written as such.

KEY CONCEPT

A ratio can increase or decrease as a result of the movement of one or both of the involved quantities.

Let's count the ways a ratio can *increase*:

1. If the top number increases while the bottom number stays relatively stable, the ratio increases.

2. If the bottom number decreases while the top number stays relatively stable, the ratio increases.

3. If both numbers increase but the price increases more, the ratio increases.

4. If both numbers decrease but the prices decrease less, the ratio increases.

A ratio decreases in just the opposite way.

KEY CONCEPT

No one ratio tells the whole story, so numerous ratios may be used. *Fundamental analysis* relies primarily on ratios, while *technical analysis* employs charts and graphs. Fundamental analysis can be further broken down into different aspects of company operations: activity, liquidity, profitability, and P/E and other ratios.

CAUTION

Interpretation of a ratio is critical. Two analysts can come to opposite conclusions by looking at the same data. Understanding the business issues involved is critical to understanding these differences in interpretation. Usually, the addition of other ratios and information clarifies the situation.

APPLICATIONS

Analyzing a company or companies through activity, liquidity, productivity, P/E, and other ratios.

PART II

4

Indexes

The Dow Jones Index is up.
The index of leading economic indicators is down.
The cost-of-living index is holding steady.

As this is being written, one of the truly sacred cows of finance and economics is under assault: the CPI, or *consumer price index*. Increasingly, economists are insisting that this important index is incorrectly calculated. This may not seem like a big deal to you, but for those who get Social Security or Federal pension payments, which are linked to the CPI, it has tremendous importance. It also determines increases in the federal tax brackets each year, to counteract "bracket creep," so we don't have to pay more in taxes just because inflation makes our salaries seem to increase more than they do.

The CPI measures what most people call the cost of living. Changes in the CPI record how much more expensive things are today than they were last month, last year, or five years ago.

If we wanted to see the price increase of just one item like, say, a pack of gum, we could simply use a percentage calculation. If gum cost .22 cents a pack one year ago and now it's .25 cents, that's an increase of 14%. (Take .25 cents minus .22 cents to get the difference, .03 cents. Then divide .03 cents by .22 cents, the starting value, to get .136. Remembering our percentage rules from the first chapter, we move the decimal two places to the right, and round to 14%.) That doesn't mean that all prices increased by 14% last year, however. Some prices may have remained constant, and others may have fallen, so it's impossible to conclude anything about the rate of inflation last year based on the price of gum. To get meaningful information about large-scale economic movements, we'll need to look at a great deal of data all at once. An index is one way of combining a broad sampling of information into a single number.

Question: What is the plural of index?

Answer: Either indices or indexes.

PURPOSE

Why do we use indexes? Because they let us *see changes in a large number of factors at once, making trends clearer*.

When we measure large-scale phenomena such as inflation, we are dealing with a large and complex set of changes. A pack of gum is, obviously, only one of hundreds of things we buy. By combining information from a number of sources, indices help us understand sweeping and complicated changes at a glance.

MAKE UP YOUR OWN INFLATION INDEX

There's no law that says you can't. What if you wanted to research inflation each day on the way to work? Call it a doughnut index. Assume for the moment that each morning you buy a cup of coffee and a couple of doughnuts on your way to work, and on reaching the office you buy a newspaper and a pack of gum in the lobby of your building. (Just play along if you take the train, buy a bagel, eat at home instead of in the car, or hate reading early in the day.)

With a little thought (very little), we determine that there are four items in our doughnut index:

one cup of coffee	.55
two doughnuts	.85
one newspaper	.35
one pack of gum	.25
sales tax	.10
Total:	$2.10

One year later, you price them again:

one cup of coffee	.45
two doughnuts	.90
one newspaper	.50
one pack of gum	.25
sales tax	.11
Total:	$2.21

Coffee was cheaper because you stopped at a new place, while the doughnuts were a little more expensive (but really good). Newspaper prices went up, and sales taxes ended up costing you more because your total was slightly higher. Your own situation may not apply to others, but it sure applies to you.

Your doughnut index increased by about 5% in one year. You first found the difference in total prices by subtracting last year's total from this year's, to get the difference of .11 cents ($2.21 minus $2.10 equals .11 cents). That's the overall increase. Then we divide this increase of .11cents by the starting amount, $2.10, to get .052 (.11 cents divided by $2.10 equals .052). Again, remembering our percentage rules from the first chapter, we move the decimal point two places to the right to get the percentage, 5.2%. Then we round to 5%.

You know your doughnut index is not a complete inflation index, because you also buy lunch and eat dinner. And, of course, you buy clothes, appliances, maybe tires, you pay rent or real estate taxes, and you sometimes take vacations. You buy a lot of stuff.

KEY CONCEPT

An index attempts to deal with *all* the items we buy, not just one or two.

The CPI is not the only index that touches our lives, directly or indirectly. There are many others, used by economists, businesses and government offices. Here's a list of the important ones:

- The *Consumer Price Index* (CPI) measures everyday consumer prices.The *Producer Price Index* (PPI), also called the wholesale price index, measures the costs of finished goods at the factory.

- The *Index of Leading Economic Indicators* measures aspects of the economy that generally predict positive or negative growth in the economy.

- The *S&P 500 Index* and The *Dow Jones Industrial Average* measure the growth of the stock market.

- The *Misery Index* measures both unemployment and inflation; if both are high, people across the country tend to be unhappy (or downright miserable) about the economy.

DEFINITION

An index is a weighted list of selected items that provide us with important economic, financial, or other statistical information. It allows us to summarize in one number how much inflation or the stock market or some other factor changes in any given period.

Our simple doughnut example didn't show the *weighting* process, so let's explore an investment problem that deals with it.

Let's say you wanted to know how much the stock market went up or down each day, and there was no Dow Jones Industrial Average or S&P 500 index. Suppose they hadn't been invented yet. How would you determine what the stock market did each day?

You might arrive at one of two solutions. One would be like our donut index: to take a few key stock prices and see how they do, assuming that they would represent in some way the whole market. The other would be to take the whole shebang—virtually all of the stocks—and follow the price changes each day. The second solution is the S&P 500 index, while the first is the Dow Jones Industrial Average.

The "S&P" in "S&P 500" stands for Standard & Poor's, a company that's involved with investment monitoring. The "500" refers to the 500 largest companies from the standpoint of the stock market; those companies' stocks are included in the S&P 500 index. In most peoples' minds, the Dow Jones Industrial Average represents the stock market, but in fact it only contains 30 stocks—although those stocks represent about 20% of the total value of the stock market. The S&P 500 contains 500 stocks (including the entire Dow Jones group) and represents about 80% of the stock market's total value.

A WEIGHTED STOCK MARKET INDEX

The S&P 500 is *weighted* according to the value and number of shares of outstanding stock of each of the 500 companies. In other words, if one company was selling for $20 and had 2 million shares outstanding, and another company was also selling for $20 but had only 1 million shares, the first company would be given twice as much weight in setting the value of the S&P index. With twice as many shares, it contributes twice as much to changes in the economy, and is therefore weighted twice as much in the index. This is how the S&P 500 works.

AN UNWEIGHTED STOCK MARKET INDEX

Since everyone has heard of the Dow Jones Industrial Average, it's well we should contrast it to the S&P 500. It contains 30 specific stocks, selected by the Dow Jones company to represent the U.S. economy as a whole. In fact, a stock with a higher dollar value does get a higher weighting, but this weighting is not as dramatic as that of the S&P 500. The **30** Dow Jones stocks are familiar company names:

AT&T	Eastman Kodak	Merck
Allied Signal	Exxon	3M
Alcoa	General Electric	Morgan, J.P.
American Express	General Motors	Philip Morris
Boeing	Goodyear	Procter & Gamble
Caterpillar	Hewlett-Packard	Sears
Chevron	IBM	Travelers Group
Coca-Cola	Johnson & Johnson	Union Carbide
Disney	International Paper	United Technologies
DuPont	McDonald's	Wal-Mart

The actual Dow Jones average is determined by adding up the prices of these companies each day and then dividing by a factor to account for stock splits over the years. The divisor is found in the *Wall Street Journal* each day. The last time I looked, January 3, 1997, the divisor was .325 (rounded). That is, you could add up the prices of each of the 30 stocks and divide by .325 and get the actual Dow Jones Industrial Average. (This divisor is listed each day at the bottom right of the Dow Jones chart.)

The Dow Jones company selects these 30 companies and makes very few changes in its list from year to year. Often the list is unchanged for years at a time. The original companies, selected in 1884, numbered only 11 and were essentially a list of railroads, which dominated the industrial landscape:

Chicago & North Western	Union Pacific
Delaware Lackawanna & Western	Missouri Pacific
Lake Shore Line	Lousiville & Nashville
New York Central	Pacific Mail
St. Paul	Western Union
Northern Pacific	

By 1886, after additions, deletions, and changes, the list consisted of 12 industrial companies:

American Cotton	Laclede Gas
American Sugar	National Lead
American Tobacco	North American
Chicago Gas	Tennessee Coal & Iron
Oil Distilling & Cattle Feeding	U.S. Leather
General Electric	U.S. Rubber

There's also now a separate list of transportation companies and utility companies.

INVESTMENT INDEXES

Although the S&P 500 and the Dow Jones are good measurements for our stock market, there are a few other indexes that deserve mentioning. Here then are all the indexes you would like to know:

For Large Capitalization Stocks

Dow Jones Industrial Average: An index of the price of 30 major industrial stocks. It is calculated by adding up the price of each stock and dividing by a certain factor to account for stock splits. There is also the Dow Jones Transportation Average, which contains the stocks of 20 airline, trucking, and railroad firms. The Dow Jones Utility Average is composed of 15 gas, electric, and power company stocks. These three averages form the Dow Jones 65 Composite Average.

Standard & Poor's 500: An index of the largest 500 domestic companies based on capitalization (price of stock times the number of outstanding shares). The S&P 500 is comprised of 400 industrials, 40 utilities, 40 financial, and 20 transportation companies.

For Smaller Capitalized Stocks

Russell 2000 and 3000: The 3000 index consists of the largest 3000 publicly traded stocks of U.S. domiciled corporations and includes both large, medium, and small capitalization stocks. It represents about 98% of the total capitalization of the New York, American, and NASDAQ market. The 2000 index is a subset of the larger 3000. The smaller index generally represents companies with a market value of $250 million or less.

Wilshire 4500 and 5000: The 5000 index includes all regularly traded domestic stocks in the United States. It excludes such stocks as Royal Shell and Unilever which are not domestically based companies. The Wilshire 5000 is the broadest of the stock market indices.

(There are about 6,000 actual individual stocks at any one time in all markets combined). The 4500 index is composed of all the domestic stocks of the United States except the largest 500 stocks, which are also known as the S&P 500. The Wilshire 4500 represents about 30% of the entire stock market, with the S&P 500 representing about 80%.

For International Stocks

EAFE: Pronounced as Ee-fah, this term stands for Europe, Australia, and the Far East. This Morgan Stanley index represents the major stock markets outside of the United States. It is composed of about 1,000 individual stocks.

For Bonds

Lehman Brothers Corporate Bond Index: A bond index that measures the total return of a diversified portfolio of corporate bonds. Thus, it represents the total return of a diversified bond fund over whatever period measured (like the S&P 500 for stocks).

Salomon Brothers Investment Bond Index: A bond index that combines U.S. Treasury and agency securities, corporate bonds mortgage-backed securities. The index is considered a good combination index, considering both income and price fluctuation. Approximately 55% of the fund is made up of U.S. Treasuries, while 20% is made up of corporate bonds, and 25% mortgage-backed securities.

WEIGHTING CONCEPT

This concept gives more emphasis, importance, or weight to certain items than others, in order to compensate for real world inequalities or to emphasize certain statistical elements.

An accountant, in trying to get a quick fix on price increases for the company's raw materials, might set up an index giving the cost of plastics a weight of 10 times that of steel, because they use 10 times more plastics than steel in their products. It would give the accountant and management an idea of their total raw material costs through a simple index. A cost increase or decrease in plastics affects them 10 times greater than in steel.

STEPS

There are really only several steps involved in constructing an index:

1. Deciding which items to use.

2. Deciding what weights to use, if any.

3. Gathering the information accurately.

4. Establishing a *base year*, or the year to start the index.

5. Periodically, (that is, monthly, quarterly, or yearly) perform simple percentage arithmetic to find the increase, or decrease in the index.

So, how do analysts know how much cabbage costs in Peoria? Gathering price information can be difficult. Usually, people are hired in different cities to go to local grocery and other stores to check them out. The CPI represents average prices throughout the country, although regional figures are also reported.

ECONOMIC DILEMMA

Coming back to the CPI problem we introduced at the beginning of this chapter: why is the CPI now considered wrong, and why is this important news for the economist? First, the CPI is considered wrong because it assumes a fixed basket of goods, as they call the products whose prices are surveyed. It assumes that even if the price of red meat goes up, consumers will still buy it, even though in the real world consumers would probably switch to fish or chicken to save money. We don't live our lives by a fixed regime, but the index assumes we do.

Secondly, the quality built into products like cars doesn't get factored in. Cars today have airbags, ABS brakes, catalytic converters, and computer chips under the hood. These innovations didn't exist in 1975, the base year for the current CPI. As a result, the cost of cars has risen faster than the cost of most other products. This increase gives the appearance of inflation, but it has more to do with the fact that cars today are actually more valuable objects than they used to be. Similar value increases have taken place in many other products, often very subtly. Inflation, remember, is an increase in price unaccompanied by an increase in value; so increases in the values of products should be factored into the CPI.

Finally, the CPI doesn't consider the cost savings of using outlets and large warehouse-type stores that are popular with consumers. These stores, which are far more common than they used to be and still proliferating, do much to counteract the price increases of various items, and to make life cheaper on the whole.

The result of all of these inaccuracies is an overstuffed CPI that makes life look more expensive than it is, and that overstates the amount of inflation that occurs each year. Economists are well aware of the ripple effect of an overestimated CPI. If the inflation numbers are wrong, so are key national statistics that are adjusted for inflation, like the gross domestic product (GDP), hourly earnings, and productivity. These numbers are all adjusted for inflation. Over many years, these small adjustments can really add up—and that means that a systematic overstatement of inflation could seriously skew the country's accounting.

Some economists now estimate that, concealed by an inaccurate CPI, our economy's gross domestic product may have increased twice as much as we thought; average worker earnings could be 35% higher than we thought; and productivity increases in this country could be three times higher. That's the power of one number. Changes in the CPI index could thus dramatically affect our economic, business, and political discussions.

Could we confirm this on our own? Can we affirm that the CPI is wrong by taking an accounting of our own life experiences? Probably only in general terms like our donut index, which is quite crude. On a broad level it's difficult to make such observations, unless we have some dramatic examples of price shifts, like the oil price shocks in the 1970s. Otherwise, changes in the cost of living are so small and gradual that we have no good nonmathematical way of seeing trends. That's why we use the CPI.

DEFINITIONS

There are two terms that are important to know when reading and discussing financial figures: *nominal* and *real*. *Nominal* means the actual number, whereas *real* is the number adjusted for inflation or other changes. There are other terms used for this, such as *adjusted for inflation* or *in real dollars*. They mean the same thing—real cost.

For instance, if an investment earned 8% interest in one year but inflation was 3%, then at the end of the year you have 8% more money, but each of your dollars is worth 3% less. Your real interest rate is really a little less than 5%. That's how much your buying power really increased during the year—your real earnings. Your buying power increases by about 5%. Your nominal interest rate may be 8%, but your real interest rate is only about 5%.

Another term to know is *in today's dollars*. If you request a statement of earnings from Social Security, (you can call them at 800-SSA-1213) the projected benefit for you is given in today's dollars. It shows what the future benefit will be without inflation—that is, compared to today.

The term *purchasing power* is also sometimes used. Let's say that our inflation base year is 1990, and five years later, in 1995, the CPI index was at 116—that is, it increased roughly 3% a year (the base year is always given a CPI value of 100). The dollar's value in 1995 is then only 86% of what it was in 1990 (100 divided by 116 equals .86 or 86%). The decrease in purchasing power would be 14% (100% minus 86% equals 14%).

USING CALCULATORS TO DETERMINE INCREASES

Using a simple hand-held calculator, we can see this increase in the index from 1990 to 1995. We are assuming an exact 3% a year increase in inflation (which is quite close to the actual CPI increases). Although we could simply multiply 3% by 5 and get 15%, we can see that because this percentage is compounded, we gain a percentage point over the 5 years:

$$100.00 \times 1.03 = 103.00$$

$$103.00 \times 1.03 = 106.09$$

$$106.09 \times 1.03 = 109.27$$

$$109.27 \times 1.03 = 112.55$$

$$112.55 \times 1.03 = 115.92$$

Notice also that we can combine two calculations into one by multiplying by 1.03, instead of first multiplying by .03 and then adding the starting number. It's a useful short-cut method to combine the two steps. In fact, you can quickly perform this calculation by one continuous calculation by just multiplying each answer by 1.03, five times.

The beauty of an index, however, is that you don't have to start with a base year of 100—you can start in any year. For instance, in the above problem, the index could have been 120 in 1990. Five years later it would be 139, if it increased at 3% per year. 120 divided by 139 gives us .86, or the same 86% we reached above.

CAUTION

Just as the accuracy of the CPI index has come into question, any numbers that come our way should be treated skeptically. We need to ask questions, like, "How were these numbers derived?" "Why were these items selected?" "Who originated these numbers?" and "What are the shortcomings of these numbers?" Numbers can be powerful tools for the careful researcher, but they can also distort and mislead, or even prove to be fundamentally incorrect. If you're wise, you will always supplement your work with indices from research of other kinds and information from other sources. As long as you use them intelligently, you can benefit considerably from indices and other mathematical tools.

QUIZ

Question 1: If an index has increased to 142, what percentage increase is this over its base year?

Question 2: If an index was 150 seven years ago and it has increased 3% each year since then, what is the value of the index today?

Answer 1: 42%. The base-year value of an index is always 100, which means that this index has increased by 42 since its base year. To find the percentage, divide the change, 42, by the original amount, 100, to get .42, or 42%.

Answer 2: 184.5, rounded. You can simply calculate this using a calculator as follows:

$$150.00 \times 1.03 = 154.50$$

$$154.50 \times 1.03 = 159.13$$

$$159.13 \times 1.03 = 163.91$$

$$163.91 \times 1.03 = 168.83$$

$$168.83 \times 1.03 = 173.89$$

$$173.89 \times 1.03 = 179.11$$

$$179.11 \times 1{,}03 = 184.48$$

SUMMARY

PURPOSE

Why do we use indexes? *Because they let us see changes in a large number of factors at once, making trends clearer.*

DEFINITION

An index is a number calculated from a usually weighted list of selected items that provide us with important economic, financial, or other information.

STEPS

There are several steps involved in constructing an index:

1. Deciding which items to use

2. Deciding what weights to use, if any

3. Gathering the information accurately

4. Establishing a *base year*, the year in which to start the index

5. Periodically (that is, monthly, quarterly, or yearly) perform simple percentage arithmetic to find the increase or decrease in the index.

KEY CONCEPTS AND RULES

- An index tries to deal with *all* the items we buy, not just one or two.

- Giving more weight to some items in a surveyed group is common, because certain items affect us more than others. If a company uses 10 times more plastic than steel, then a cost index for that company would probably weight, or multiply, the cost of plastics by 10.

DEFINITIONS

Nominal values are the actual or named numbers, whereas *real* values are numbers adjusted for inflation or other changes. The term "in today's dollars" means a future number without inflation, which makes it easier to compare to prices or costs today. The term "purchasing power" is used to show the erosion of the value of something considering inflation.

CAUTION

As we can see from the hubbub surrounding the CPI, the devil is in the details. Question the assumptions behind numbers and the weights given to each item, if any.

APPLICATIONS

Economics, accounting, investments, finance, and politics.

5

Break-Even Analysis

Are we making any money?
Who needs a profit anyway?

The big question for any business is: "Are we making any money?" Some would argue that it's more complex. Employees might say that a business exists to provide jobs. A community could assert that a business exists to help the community. A consumer would say that a business is there to provide products and services. Perhaps they are all correct. But the fundamental fact of life is, if a business is not making money, then it will go out of business, and employees will be looking for work elsewhere.

PURPOSE

The purpose of a business enterprise is to make money, meaning profits, so that it can continue to exist.

DEFINITION

A *profit* is the money made by a business over and above expenses. It is that money that can pay bonuses or be put back into the business to expand the business further.

Break-even analysis is study intended to determine the point at which, for every additional product or service rendered, a company makes a profit. Up to that point, the company loses money. Thereafter, the company makes money, assuming that costs and customers remain stable.

Example: McSoftware Inc.

Let's say our company, McSoftware Inc., makes software to keep track of engineering projects. We have programmers to develop the software further, technical support people to answer questions that the manual covered poorly or skipped, a few others who ship the software and do miscellaneous things, and a small group of managers to run the place. Let's say fifteen people in all.

We have an outside firm that physically puts the software package together. They make copies of the software, print the manual, design the box for it, and ship it to us for final shipment to our customers. Since we sell our software through the mail, we only produce the software packages when we have orders. It's a simple business with fixed and variable expenses.

DEFINITION

Fixed costs, or expenses, are in general the costs we have regardless of how many units we sell. Variable costs, or expenses, are the additional expenses for each unit we sell.

In our case, we have a number of fixed costs. We rent office space, and the landlord expects a check each month. We need electricity for lights, computers and everything else a modern company uses, like fax machines, coffee machines, and so forth. We pay the phone bill. We have to pay the salaries of our programmers, tech staff, office staff, and managers.

We also have *variable costs*. There is a cost for each software package we sell. In the extreme case, which we really don't want to think about, if we didn't sell any software packages, our variable costs would be zero. That is, we would never have to spend any money on manufacturing, packaging or shipping the software. (Actually, we would probably accumulate an inventory of packages even before we received orders, to have them ready to ship—but you get the idea.)

We also had *startup costs*—computers to buy, along with desks, chairs, bookshelves, and decorations to make the office presentable.

Those are one-time expenses that are relevant only to startup concerns. For now, we're just dealing with ongoing costs.

Let's see what our total costs are for various levels of sales:

NUMBER OF UNITS SOLD	FIXED COSTS	VARIABLE COSTS	TOTAL COSTS
500	$600,000	$50,000	$650,000
750	$600,000	$75,000	$675,000
1,000	$600,000	$100,000	$700,000
1,200	$600,000	$120,000	$720,000
1,250	$600,000	$125,000	$725,000
1,500	$600,000	$150,000	$750,000

We've used increments of 250 units starting at 500, except that we've already calculated that 1,200 units was of particular importance (we'll explain that shortly), so we added that to our table, too. To find our break-even point, we'll graph our situation so we can visually observe our business possibilities.

STEPS

1. First, plot the fixed costs.

2. Next, plot the variable costs on top of fixed costs.

3. Finally, plot the sales, or revenues.

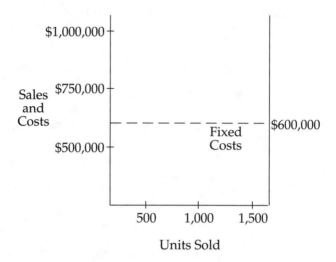

Units Sold

First we plot the fixed costs. In our example, they are $600,000. Here we use a straight line, and you'll notice that we're using a dotted line, so that when we add the other lines we'll keep our fixed costs clearly in mind. The fixed costs line shows that no matter how many units of software we sell, our fixed costs will still be $600,000.

As a company would increase its production beyond a certain point, these fixed costs might increase. That is, if the business is so successful that additional programmers are needed, and a bigger office is necessary, and more computers are required, then the fixed costs go up. In the real world, there are creeping incremental increases in fixed costs if a company is growing. A company doesn't just go from 15 to 50 people overnight. Often a few people are added each year, and after a few years, where there used to be 15 people in a rented flat, there are 50 people in a new building.

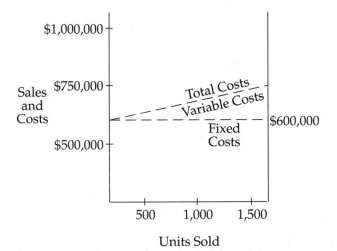

Units Sold

Next, we add our variable costs to the diagram. We add it on top of the fixed costs so we can see the resultant total costs at one time. Thus, we start plotting the variable costs where the fixed costs start, in this case $600,000. If we just wanted to plot the variable costs and nothing else, we would start at zero and work our way up.

In our example, after 1,500 units are sold, our variable costs total $150,000; that's a $100 cost for each unit produced. We add this number to our fixed costs of $600,000 to obtain our total costs of $750,000.

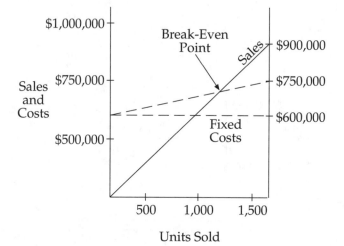

Finally, we finish our diagram by plotting the income side, the sales, or revenues. In our example we sold each software package for $600. After selling 1,000 units, we realized $600,000 ($600 times 1,000 equals $600,000) in total sales. After selling 1,500 units, we realized $900,000 ($600 times 1,500 equals $900,000).

By plotting sales in the same chart with our costs, we can see where we make a profit—the point where we get to break out the champagne, if for only a brief celebration. This point, where our sales line crosses our total costs line, is the break-even point, or champagne point. Thereafter, it's good times ahead, more or less.

In our example, we can also see the figures and calculate this point by trial and error, as below. In chapter 9 on algebra, we'll show you how you can solve for this break-even point mathematically.

NUMBER OF UNITS SOLD	TOTAL SALES	COSTS	PROFIT
500	$300,000	$650,000	($350,000)
750	450,000	675,000	(225,000)
1,000	600,000	700,000	(100,000)
1,200	720,000	720,000	0
1,250	750,000	725,000	25,000
1,500	900,000	750,000	150,000

To show a negative result, you can either use a minus sign or parentheses, like this:

-$350,000

($350,000)

I prefer to use parentheses because they highlight the results, whereas the little minus sign might not get your full attention.

THE ADVANCED BREAK-EVEN CHART

In the real world, we may not be able to charge $600 for each unit. Maybe our competitor reduces a similar package to $550, and we respond by lowering our price. Maybe our product is so good we can charge a premium for it, and we realize $650 per unit.

Costs can change as well as prices. Our fixed costs can decrease if we feel we don't need some of the programmers, or increase if we need more. Variable costs can change, with a new supplier that promises to deliver them to us for $90 rather than $100, saving us money.

Management wants to maintain a stable profit margin, or even increase it, if possible. If additional costs, fixed or variable, are planned for, the break-even chart can be recalculated to see how profitability will be affected. If, for instance, the software is receiving good reviews in engineering magazines and business is picking up, our costs may go up as well. More staff is needed. However, we may decide not to add staff and try to get by on our company of 15. Perhaps our customers will start to complain and our sales may fall off. Perhaps if we request too many units from our outside vendor, the quality drops. The manual might be missing in some units, or the software disks were too cheap to stand up to wear and tear and caused our clients' problems. These, and other, real life situations are what management and companies deal with each day.

What can result is a break-even chart that could look like this:

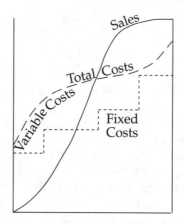

Different companies in different industries would have different break-even charts, but illustrated here is a company that experiences step-increases in fixed costs, variable costs fluctuate as to volume of units produced, and the selling price is estimated to fluctuate with volume as well.

ADVANCED FIXED AND VARIABLE COSTS

Another difficulty is classifying costs as either fixed or variable, but in many companies there might not be as clear-cut a distinction. Some are partly fixed and variable, often called semivariable by accountants. Perhaps a company has an idle plant that is used for seasonal increases in volume. The idle plant may be less efficient and will require additional costs when put into service.

Multiple products or services are also a norm for companies and there may be a number of break-even charts for each product or service.

Also, company taxes need to be incorporated into these figures and thus accountants will fine tune the numbers.

Finally, the costs used are usually historical. Past and current costs are used, but the future may be different. Perhaps management can anticipate some trends and build them in the chart, or perhaps as things change in the marketplace, the charts will need to be redone.

CALCULATORS

We've used simple hand-held calculators for these calculations, and hopefully you've duplicated the results along with us. Nothing fancy, just straight adding, subtracting, and multiplying.

QUIZ

Question 1: Given our example of our project software selling for $600, what is the break-even point if everything stayed the same, but we had to reduce the price to $550?

Question 2: Given our example of our project software selling for $600 a unit, let's say we're able to decrease our fixed costs by $50,000. We were able to move to another office location and now our fixed costs are only $550,000, versus the previous $600,000. What is the break-even point if everything else is the same?

Answer 1: 1,334 units would be the break-even point, versus our old 1,200 units. To verify this, our sales would be $733,700 ($550 times 1,334). Our costs would be $733,400 ($600,000 fixed costs plus $133,400 variable costs—$100 times 1,334 units). You can arrive at this answer through trial and error, or algebra which we demonstrate in chapter 9.

Answer 2: 1,100 units would be the break-even point, versus our old 1,200 units. To verify this, our sales would be $660,000 ($600 times 1,100). Our costs would now be $660,000 ($550,000 fixed costs plus $110,000 variable costs - $100 times 1,100 units). You can arrive at this answer through trial and error, or algebra which we demonstrate in chapter 9.

SUMMARY

PURPOSE

The purpose of a business enterprise is to make money, meaning profits, so that it can continue to exist.

DEFINITIONS

- A *profit* is the money over and above expenses.

- *Break-even analysis* is a study to determine the point at which, for every additional product or service rendered, a company makes a profit.

- *Fixed costs*, or expenses, are in general the costs we have regardless of how many units we sell.

- *Variable costs*, or expenses, are the additional expenses for each unit we sell.

STEPS

1. First, plot the fixed expenses.

2. Next, plot the variable expenses on top of fixed costs.

3. Finally, plot the sales, or revenues.

BASIC AND ADVANCED CONCEPTS

In our example of McSoftware, Inc., we tried to show the basics of determining the break-even point. In the real world, costs and sales are not so easy to forecast.

CAUTION

Break-even analysis can be quite complex. Fixed costs can go up in steps as volume increases. Variable costs may not be a straight line, it may be curved or jump up or down at certain points.

APPLICATIONS

Accounting, analyzing an ongoing business, calculating the profitability of a new business, marketing analysis for new products, and general analysis of companies for banking purposes.

CHAPTER

6

Curves and
Diagrams

If a picture is worth a thousand words, a curve or diagram is worth a whole report.

Let's start with two definitions: concave and convex curves. Think of a *concave curve* as the entrance to a cave or mine (or the McDonald's arches):

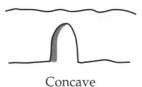

Concave

Thus, any curve that goes up and bends to the right is some form of concave curve. Consider these variations:

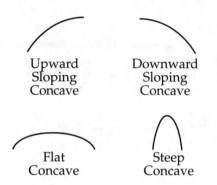

Upward
Sloping
Concave

Downward
Sloping
Concave

Flat
Concave

Steep
Concave

The opposite is a *convex curve* that is shaped like the letter U:

Convex
(like the letter U)

Variations can look like any of these:

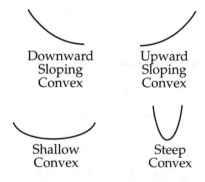

Downward
Sloping
Convex

Upward
Sloping
Convex

Shallow
Convex

Steep
Convex

If a curve seems like a straight line, neither concave nor convex, then it's just a line without a name.

PURPOSE AND DEFINITION OF A CURVE

A *curve* represents a visual relationship. Whereas a graph represents basic quantitative information, a curve or diagram shows a relationship, like the one between supply and demand. A curve shows how that relationship changes as the variables change.

Example: Supply and Demand

At the core of economy and business, and indeed many aspects of life, is the interaction between supply and demand. These terms tend to crop up in the explanation of almost any large-scale social or economic process. "The reason it's priced at $40 per unit is because of the law of supply and demand," "Companies won't make more because the demand isn't there," and "If we demand more, the supply will surely follow."

DEFINITONS

Demand is the consumer's desire to buy a commodity, while *supply* is the production of that commodity for sale.

Demand is a representation of the quantity of a commodity wanted at a specific price. If we desire to be involved with the Internet, then it is said that the demand for the Internet has increased. The *law* of demand says the lower the price of something, the greater the demand for it.

Supply is the representation of the amount of goods and services a company is willing to produce at various prices. The *law* of supply says: the higher the price of something, the greater the supply will be. This agrees with our common sense, as well as our business sense. The more popular an item is, the higher the price that can be charged, the higher the profit, thus more companies will produce more of it.

Although we can discuss supply and demand *ad nauseam*, we'll understand it better by simply drawing a curve. First, let's look at the demand curve:

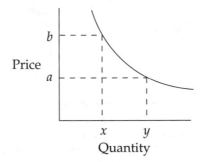

The demand curve shows that the lower the price (a), the greater the demand by consumers (y). (It's a downward sloping convex curve.) This, of course, makes sense to us. We as consumers will demand more wine, for example, if the price is lower.

The supply curve is the opposite. (It's an upward sloping convex curve.)

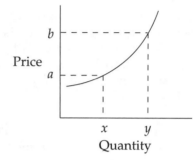

The supply curve shows that the greater the price (b), the greater supply by companies (y). This makes sense. You as a business person will increase the supply (by producing more of a product) if the price you can get is higher. It means more profit for you.

At any point in time, these two market forces may reach a compromise, if only temporarily, and give rise to a generally agreed-upon price for a product or service. When put together, they form the *supply and demand curve*:

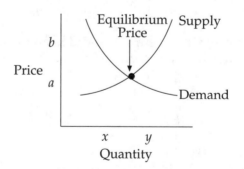

The point where the two curves intercept is called the *equilibrium price*, that point where the market forces are in equilibrium, at a given point in time. When the price for Internet access was lowered to $20 a month recently, consumer demand increased dramatically, and all online providers had to fall in line, or fall off the table.

HISTORICAL PERSPECTIVE

1776, a year we remember in America for its importance in our political history, was also a year of revolution in the ideas of free markets. Adam Smith published his *Wealth of Nations*, asserting that governments did not have to regulate the marketplace to make it work. The system, he argued, could take care of itself.

The essence of free markets, markets governed by supply and demand, is that prices regulate the markets. The lower the price, the greater the demand but the lower the supply. The higher the price, the less the demand but the higher the supply. Markets have built-in counterbalancing forces.

If the supply of a commodity exceeds demand, then prices drop. If demand exceeds supply, then prices increase. "Cabbage Patch" dolls in the 1980s were a good example of demand outpacing supply, and the dolls, where they could be found, were sold at a premium. The latest exaggeration in demand surrounded the "Tickle-Me Elmo" doll.

There are, of course, exceptions. Sometimes, a maker of a product may appeal to the snob in others (never in us, of course). If a wine maker deliberately priced a wine higher it might lead people to believe that it was better, with resulting higher sales.

DEFINITION OF ELASTICITY

A basic economic concept, *elasticity* refers to how variable, or stretchable, demand or supply is in response to price increases or decreases. If demand, or supply, is very sensitive to changes in prices, then it's considered elastic. If it's not very sensitive to price changes, then it's inelastic.

The following curves illustrate this relationship for demand:

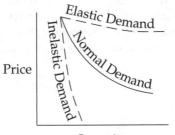

Quantity

The graph shows a "normal" demand curve, and superimposes representations of elastic and inelastic relationships. The elastic curve shows that little changes in price produce considerable increases in demand. Computers are an example. As the prices of computers have decreased, there has been a tremendous increase in demand for them.

The inelastic curve shows the opposite: changes in prices followed by little change in demand. When a product is "hot," there can be considerable inelasticity of demand. Harley-Davidson motorcycles are a good example. The prices of these popular bikes have actually increased, but demand for them continues to rise regardless. The company can't make them fast enough. People commonly wait two years or longer for new motorcycles. Demand has failed to decrease in response to price increases.

A similar relationship can be shown for the supply curve:

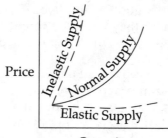

Quantity

The supply of internet Web sites has increased dramatically, even though the price of getting online has stabilized at the presently universal $20.00 monthly charge. The supply is elastic. An example of an inelastic supply would be the supply of turkeys available at Thanksgiving. Even if prices for turkeys went up, the supply probably wouldn't change very much.

Example: Yield Curve

To investors, one of the most closely watched curves is the *yield curve* of Treasury issues. It shows the relationship between the length of maturity and interest rates. Usually, the longer the maturity, the higher the interest rates, as shown in the following *Wall Street Journal* excerpt:

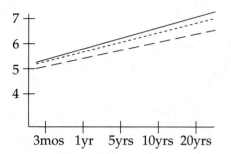

Yield Curve

It actually shows three curves, the solid-line being the most current, the less solid line a week ago, and the dotted line a year ago. The recent and one-year comparisons show movements in interest rates.

The current curve shows that short-term interest rates are about 5.2%. That is, any money you invest in a money market mutual fund should be earning about this interest. At the other extreme, long-term interest rates are about 6.75% and have risen about 25 basis points since last year. A basis point is a technical unit equal to one-hundredth of a percentage, so that an increase of 30 basis points represents a change of three-tenths of a percent.

This long-term interest rate is related to inflation expectations and also relates closely to mortgage rates. Thirty-year fixed-rate mortgages are usually about 50 basis points, or one-half a percentage point, higher than the Treasury Bond rate.

Example: Bell-Shaped Curve

It's the most common curve in statistics. It represents the normal distribution of so many business activities. It is sometimes called appropriately, the normal curve. There are a surprising number of examples of bell-shaped type distributions not only in business, but in our everyday lives.

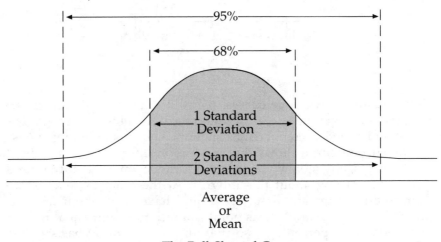

Average
or
Mean

The Bell-Shaped Curve

The center is technically called the mean, although the term average is more commonly used among nonstatisticians. The shaded area of one standard deviation represents about 68% of all events, or about two-thirds of the time the events will be within this area. Two standard deviations represents about 95% of all events, three standard deviations, 99%.

The chapters on statistics cover this diagram in some detail.

Example: The Westbrook Curve

Finally, let me share with you a curve I've often explained to my executive friends:

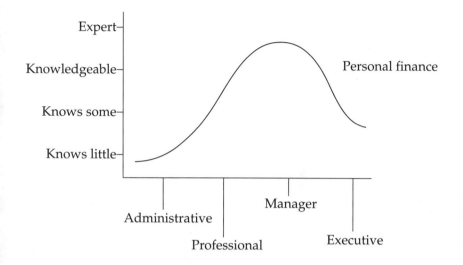

The Westbrook Curve

It shows a relationship between knowledge of personal financial and retirement issues versus how high you are in a company hierarchy. There are exceptions, of course, as in most areas of knowledge. Starting from the bottom of the organization and going up, there is increasing amounts of knowledge, reaching the highest within middle management. But my direct experience has taught me that as I continue up through the executive ranks, there is a decreasing level of knowledge!

Explanation? Executives are fully capable of understanding personal finance, as much if not more than others. They, however, are too busy running companies to be able to spend very much time dealing with and learning about this subject.

7

Graphs and Presenting Math Information

A good visual is worth 1,000 words.

A poor visual raises 1,000 questions.

Graphs, curves, charts, and diagrams are all visual presentations of information. They are also terms used quite broadly in the financial industry. A *graph* usually shows relationships among numbers. It can be a progression of numbers, like sales figures in a line graph. It can be pieces of the whole, like a pie chart.

A *curve* usually shows the relationship between two different things, like supply and demand. A *chart* is the most general and can mean just about any visual display that contains information. Some graphs are even called charts, like pie charts. A *diagram* is usually pictorial, and shows how something works or clarifies relationships between parts of a whole.

Graphs abound in the business world, especially because today's software makes it easy to create complex graphical illustrations at will. Spreadsheet programs all have this capability, and many word-processing applications can create graphs as well. Specialized graphical software can be used to put together really eye-popping visuals.

The most frequently used graphs are line graphs, bar charts, and pie charts. Sometimes two graph types are combined, as in a line-and-bar chart. There are even logarithmic graphs. Here are the types of graphs you'll most often come in contact with:

 Line graph shows change over time

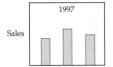 **Bar graph** or chart compares values to one another

 Pie Chart shows individual values to the whole

 Combination Chart

 3-D Graphs

Pie

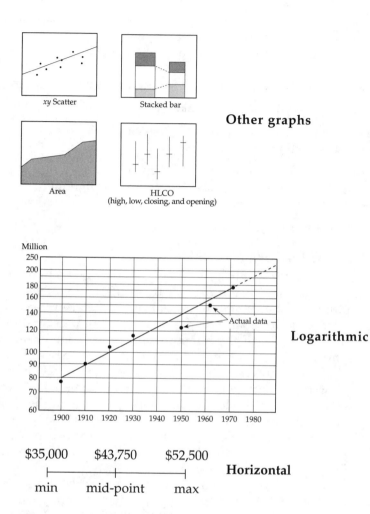

xy Scatter

Stacked bar

Area

HLCO
(high, low, closing, and opening)

Other graphs

Million

Logarithmic

Actual data

$35,000 $43,750 $52,500

min   mid-point   max

Horizontal

PURPOSE AND DEFINITION

A *graph* is a visual representation of information, which usually provides an easier way to understand that information.

KEY POINT

The real question is: What do you want to show, demonstrate, or prove? Because graphing information can now be done with a click of your mouse, it's easier than ever to overuse this presentation tool. Ask yourself what you're trying to show. Does a graph help you prove your point, or does it primarily prove that your office software can generate pretty graphs? If you're not sure, the tried-and-true method is to check with your peers, within or outside your company, for their opinions. In a glut of graphs or charts, your main point can get lost.

There are really only a few things to remember about graphing:

1. Double-check your data to make sure it's accurate.

2. Try several types of graphs to see which provides the clearest depiction of your information.

3. Listen to the questions you get when people see the graph. They will tell you how the graph is communicating or failing to communicate.

4. Don't overuse graphs.

PRESENTING MATH INFORMATION

Here's your mission, Mr. Phelps, should you choose to accept it (and remember, your boss said you'd present this stuff, and you want to keep your job): How should you represent typical salary ranges, or the newer concept of broadband ranges, in a report or presentation?

You might not be part of the human resources or compensation department, but go along with us as we see how we can assist in a presentation with charts. The subject of salary range broadbands is currently a hot topic within compensation and human resource circles. A good summary article on this subject appears in the *ACA Journal*, Autumn 1994, by Kenan S. Abosch and Janice S. Hand, page 6.

Normally, there are about 10 or 12 salary ranges for professional employees within a company (this does not apply to hourly employees or executives). That is, from a trainee fresh out of college to professional-level and management people in an organization, there are typically about a dozen overlapping pay ranges. A typical salary range might be, for instance, from $35,000 to $52,500.

A range usually has a 50% spread. That is, in our example just above, $35,000 is the minimum, and the maximum is 50% higher, or $52,500. An easy way to calculate the maximum, as we explain in more detail in the next chapter, is to enter $35,000 into your calculator (the simple hand-held type) and multiply by 1.5. The answer will be $52,500. Multiplying by 1.5 produces a number 50% higher than the original value.

Further, professional salary ranges start at about $25,000 for entry-level workers and increase to about $150,000 for those on the cusp of executive-hood. Each range usually starts about a third of the way up from the minimum end of the range below it. For instance, if one range runs from $35,000 to $52,500, then the next range would start about $41,000 (rounded). To verify this, find the spread of the lower range, which in this case is $17,500 ($52,500 minus $35,000 equals $17,500). Then divide by 3 to get $5,833 and add $35,000 (the minimum) to get $40,833. Rounding, you get $41,000. So the next range would start at about $41,000 and go to $61,500 (multiply $41,000 by 1.5). Then repeat the steps to obtain the next range, and so forth.

A salary broadband is larger than a regular salary range–much larger. Instead of the maximum being 50% greater than the minimum, it can be 100% or even 200% greater. Thus a company could have only three broadband salary ranges for professionals:

Salary range 1: $25,000 to $60,000

Salary range 2: $50,000 to $100,000

Salary range 3: $85,000 to $150,000

Although still in its infancy as a compensation structure (if it catches on at all), broadbanding is designed to complement a more modern concept of the workforce as a body of flexible employees working in teams.

The question we are addressing here is: How should we show these ranges in any report or presentation material?

VISUAL INTUITION

Start by examining how people usually see a range, if they visualize it. In human resource and compensation circles, a range is usually represented by a set of horizontal lines showing the minimum, midpoint, and the maximum:

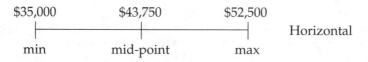

This seems to pass the intuitive test, meaning that we can easily understand the range when it's displayed horizontally. It could also be shown vertically, but may not be as intuitively accessible as a horizontal line.

The next question would be how to show the difference between the typical dozen ranges and the comparatively few broadband ranges. My preference would be for the horizontal format, but you decide:

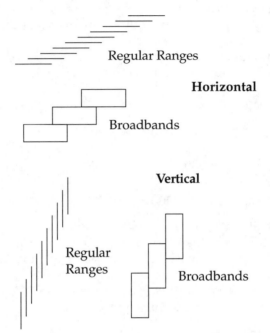

Regular Ranges

Horizontal

Broadbands

Vertical

Regular Ranges

Broadbands

The real question is how to design a graph, chart, curve, or diagram in a way that appeals to our visual intuition. You want your chart to communicate quickly, so you can make your point without confusing or distracting your audience. A chart that doesn't work with people's visual instincts simply slows readers down, and at worst derails your communication.

There are really only a few questions to ask when putting together a graph or chart of mathematical information:

1. Is the information presented intuitively?

2. After trying several charts, which one communicates most instinctively?

Finally, if you're not sure how best to present your data graphically, prepare the information several ways and check with business associates you respect for their opinions. The final word:

A good visual is worth 1,000 words.
A poor visual raises 1,000 questions.

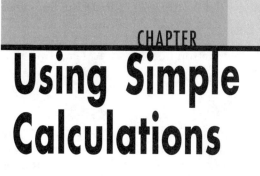

Using Simple Calculations

So, three guys rented a hotel room for $30, each chipping in $10. The next morning, the owner told the clerk that he charged them too much, the room cost only $25. The clerk put $2 in his pocket and gave each guy $1 back. But if the guys had then paid $27 (3 times $9) and the clerk kept $2, where's the other dollar? The answer is at end of chapter, but there is an easy solution to this problem: the hand-held calculator. The basic model can be had for as little as $2 in some places; nicer ones go for as much as $15. After the pencil, it's the basic mathematical tool of the businessperson.

Simple calculators are our concern here—not those complicated, computer-like calculators with dozens of special keys. In a later chapter, we'll discuss computer spreadsheets, which are closely related to those engineering and scientific calculators.

What amazes me about simple hand-held calculators, which are on every desk, is that their memory and percentage functions are almost never used by the average person. After I explain these functions, especially the "M" (memory) keys, people genuinely thank me. They've discovered something useful that's been hidden right under their noses. Unfortunately, those tiny booklets that come with the calculators, if they're not discarded out of hand, are difficult to read, let alone understand. For now, get a calculator in front of you, along with its instruction booklet, if you can find it, and let's review the "M" keys.

MEMORY KEYS

There are usually three memory keys, commonly labeled M+, M-, and MR (or something similar). These are for memory add, subtract, and recall. Sometimes there is a fourth key that erases memory, labeled differently on different calculators. In most calculators with only three M keys, you erase memory by pressing the MR key twice. Since some calculators label their keys differently you will need to check your instruction booklet for specifics. Here is a summary of the standard memory key functions:

M+/M- (memory add/memory subtract) keys: When you press the M+ key on a basic calculator, the number currently shown in the calculator's display will be saved in memory. Many basic calculator models will retain a number in memory even after the calculator is turned off. If you perform another calculation and want to add the second answer to the number you've stored, then press M+ again. The memory now contains the sum of the two numbers. If you want to subtract the second calculation from the first, then press the M- key instead of the M+ key. When you press the MR key, the resulting number is recalled from memory and shown on the calculator's display.

MR (memory recall) key: Whenever you wish to recall the number in memory, simply press the MR key. Even after your calculator has been turned off, this number should still be in memory (it can last as long as the battery lasts). When a number is stored in memory, most calculators display an "M" somewhere in the calculator window. The "M" stays there as long as there is some number in the memory.

Memory erase: To erase memory, usually you press the MR key twice. Sometimes there is a separate key to erase memory.

KEEPING A CONSTANT IN THE CALCULATOR

As we discussed in chapter 2, if you're traveling to a foreign country and want to keep track of the factor that converts a foreign currency into American dollars, simply enter the conversion factor and press the M+ key.

For instance, let's say you were going to Paris, and the conversion rate of francs to dollars was 1 to .19, meaning that one franc equals 19 cents. You would than enter .19 (for 19 cents) into your calculator and press the M+ key. You would then have, for the duration of your trip, the value .19 stored in your calculator's memory (until you erase it or add another number to it). If that scarf along the Champs Elysées costs 125 francs, simply enter 125, press the ×key (for multiplying), press the MR key (where .19 is saved), and then press the = key. Voilá, it's $23.75. You now know whether the scarf is a bargain.

Percent (%) Key: Simple calculators often have a % key. Although I usually recommend that you simply multiply by the actual percentage amount, let's use the % key. Say you work for a store that usually marks up prices 50%—a typical markup. If the wholesale price of an item (that's the price the store pays for the item) is $25, what is the price to the consumer after a 50% markup?

Enter 25 (for $25), press the ×key (for multiplying), then enter 50 and press the % key. Your answer should say 12.50. Most, but not all, calculators that have the % key work this way. Sometimes there is actually a markup key, usually named MU. You'll need to check the calculator's instructions to be sure how to use it.

MOST USEFUL MULTIPLIER

In this markup problem, you really want to find the retail price to charge your customers. You can therefore use one of the most useful single-step methods available. Enter 25 (for $25 as before), press the × key for multiplying, enter 1.5, and then press the = key. The answer is $37.50. What did we do? We actually found 50% of the original price and added it to 100%, the original price, all in one step. The 1.5 represents 150%; 100% for the original price and 50% for the markup. If you wanted to mark up an item of merchandise by 20%, you would multiply by 1.2, or 120%. And so on.

POWERS WITHOUT A POWER KEY

Suppose you wanted to find 5^5, meaning $5 \times 5 \times 5 \times 5 \times 5$, or 5 times itself 5 times. Most simple calculators allow the following: Enter 5, press the ×key, then press the = sign four times. Your answer is 3,125. Each time you press the equal sign, it repeats the last calculation you made, which in this case was multiplication by 5. The actual steps should look like this:

$$5 \times 5 = 25$$
$$= 125$$
$$= 625$$
$$= 3,125$$

Keep pressing the = key and you keep multiplying by the first number. Remember that the first power is the number itself, so we only pressed the = key four times to get 5 to the fifth power–not five times. As another example, suppose you wanted the eighth power of 4, or 4^8. You would enter 4, press the ×key, and press the = key seven times. The answer is 65,536.

CHECKING YOUR ADDITION

Because some numbers need to be absolutely correct, here's an accountant's method to make sure of your work. If you're adding a string of numbers, do them a second time by adding them backward. Start at the bottom and work your way up. Both answers should, obviously, be the same. Adding the list in reverse the second time should prevent you from repeating any careless errors you night have made the first time.

ROUNDING ANSWERS

It's not always easy to know when to round a number. Sometimes the actual number, with all its digits, is necessary and appropriate. An engineer needs to be precise. But sometimes a rounded number serves a better function, such as when the focus is on the magnitude of the number (its size) more than the precise value. That's where too many digits can get in the way of clear communication. For instance: the population of the U.S. is about 260 million people. For most discussions, we don't need the precise number, even if someone could determine it precisely. (In fact, the census department believes that its count is usually several million people short!)

Rounding can also be helpful if you want to check an answer. If you're multiplying 924 by 49, you can make sure you're in the right ballpark by multiplying 1,000 by 50. In this case, the answer should be about 50,000. It's a good way to ascertain that your number is about right. Sometimes an answer is off by a decimal place, which would make your answer ten times too large or two small, an error that this checking method usually catches.

IS MY CALCULATOR ACCURATE?

Presumably it is, but there's an easy way to find out. Enter 1 in your calculator and divide by 1.333. Your answer should be .7501875, depending on how many decimal places your calculator's display shows. Now, multiply that number by 1.333 and you should get all 9s. In a normal 8-digit display, a calculator usually shows 9s instead of a 1. It would need a 10-place display to show a 1. When you do this calculation, your calculator may show some 8s at the end, instead of all 9s. It's accurate to that point, and it rounds thereafter.

WHY DO I GET AN "E"?

An answer with a capital "E" means that your result is so small or large that the calculator can't display it all. You might get an answer like 4.04E-10. This is scientific notation, a way of rounding off and displaying very large numbers. The expression 4.04E-10 means that you can approximate the correct answer by taking 4.04 and moving the decimal point 10 places to the left. In this case, the result of your calculation is actually something like 40,400,000,000, or more than forty billion. Sometimes a very simple calculator will freak out during massive calculations and display a one or a zero instead of a number in scientific notation. But then, you should use a computer to work with such large numbers.

CHECK PREVIOUS CHAPTERS

To see some of the practical benefits of good calculator skills, you might like to review these sections:

- A tax calculation in chapter 1, p. 9
- Currency conversions in chapter 2, p. 19
- Ratios in chapter 3, p. 31-32
- Indexes in chapter 4, p. 44

HOW BIG A NUMBER DO YOU WANT?

This stuff might be a little too lofty for your calculator, but since we're talking about numbers, do you know what the biggest official number is? It was at one time the "googol." Reportedly named by an infant, the googol is a 1 with 100 zeros behind it. In math circles it is written as 10^{100}. It dwarfs the biggest numbers we normally think of, such as a trillion or a quadrillion, which are only 10^{12} and 10^{15}.

That number has now been overshadowed by the googolplex, which is defined as 10^{googol}. This is supposed to be greater than the number of atomic particles in the universe, but who's counting? I once heard an alternative definition of a googolplex: 1 with as many zeros you can write before you give up. (It doesn't have to be finished in one sitting.)

Most people, in their math naivete, would say that "infinity" is the largest number, but infinity isn't a number at all. If infinity were a number, then it wouldn't be infinity, since any number can be counted to, given enough time, but infinity is unreachable by definition. If you'd like an interesting discussion of infinity check out the mega-math web site by the Los Alamos National Laboratory at: www.c3.lanl.gov/mega-math. Click on Hotel Infinity.

A FINAL CAUTION

Calculating numbers blindly can lead to blind conclusions. Always review your answer to ensure that it makes sense. If you are trying to find 10% of 555 and you get 5, perhaps your decimal point has been misplaced. Never stop using your head just because you're using a calculator.

ANSWER: NUMERICAL ILLUSION

Let's review the "math joke" introduced at the top of the chapter:

Three guys rented a hotel room for $30 by chipping in $10 each. The next morning, the owner told the clerk that he had charged the three too much, as the room cost only $25. The clerk then pocketed $2 and gave each guy $1 back. If the three guys had then paid $27 (3 times $9) and the clerk kept $2, where's the other dollar?

The answer is that we make a false assumption by trying to relate the answer to $30. When the clerk gave back $3 dollars, we should relate the answer to $27, not $30. The three men paid $27, and of that sum the clerk has $2 and the owner has $25. Everything is accounted for.

Why do we try to relate the answer to $30? Because we have $30 in our mind. The story begins with $30 so it seems plausible to consider the answer in relation to that amount. It's a numerical illusion.

A FINAL GREETING

To end this chapter on an even lighter note, enter the number 3.0936 in your calculator and divide by 4. If you turn your calculator upside down, you get my friendly greeting to you.

9

Algebra

Algebra, the language of math, uses letters and symbols to express a whole range of problems and solutions. Algebra expresses general relationships that can apply to any set of specific numbers. It's a fundamental tool of business math.

THE BASIC RULES

1. The result of addition is a *sum*.

2. The result of subtraction is a *difference*.

3. The result of multiplication is a *product*.

4. The result of division is a *quotient*.

On paper, we represent multiplication in different ways: sometimes with the symbols ($\times$) or ($\bullet$), and sometimes simply by placing two quantities side by side, implying that they are to be multiplied. We usually represent division with a line:

Multiplying	Dividing
$2 \times 4 = 8$	$\dfrac{8}{2} = 4$
$2 \bullet 4 = 8$	
$2(3 + 1) = 8$	$\dfrac{n + 4}{n} = 4$
$2n = 8$	

Signed numbers follow clear rules. In both multiplication and division, if two numbers have the same sign, then the answer is positive. If the numbers have opposite signs, then the answer is negative. When numbers are positive, we often do not show signs, as the assumption is that they are positive.

Multiplying	Dividing	
$(-5)(4) = -20$	$\dfrac{20}{4} = 5$	$\dfrac{-20}{-4} = 5$
$-5(4) = -20$		
$5(-4) = -20$	$\dfrac{-20}{4} = -5$	$\dfrac{20}{-4} = -5$
$-5(-4) = +20$		

Odd powers of negative numbers are negative. Even powers of negative numbers are positive:

$$(-3)^3 = (-3)(-3)(-3) = -27$$
$$(-3)^4 = (-3)(-3)(-3)(-3) = 81$$

Parentheses and brackets keep algebraic operations organized. Do the operations within the parentheses first, then work outwards. Powers, or exponents, of an expression are performed before products:

$$x = 5 + \{10 (4 + 2)^2\}$$
$$x = 5 + \{10 (6)^2\}$$
$$x = 5 + \{10 (36)\}$$
$$x = 5 + \{360\}$$
$$x = 365$$

A term is a cluster of one or more numbers and variables connected by multiplication or division. An expression is one or more terms connected by addition or subtraction. An equation is a statement of equality between two algebraic expressions.

$$\text{terms:} \quad 2, a, 5, x^2$$

$$\text{an expression:} \quad 2(a+5) + x^2$$

$$\text{an equation:} \quad 2(a+5) + x^2 = y$$

A *coefficient* is a constant (that is, a number—they're called con-stants because their values don't change), or a term, before a vari-able. If there is no coefficient, then the variable's coefficient is assumed to be 1.

An *independent variable* is the variable that drives the relation expressed in a formula or equation. Changes in the independent variable will produce changes in the rest of the relation. The *depen-dent variable* is the variable determined by the independent variable. Its value will change in response to changes in the independent variable. Usually, the variable x is designated as the independent variable, while y is usually the dependent variable. Sometimes the equation is written to emphasize the independent x variable, like this: $f(x) = 2x$. The expression reads, "the function of x equals $2x$." Here's an example of these variables in an equation and its graph:

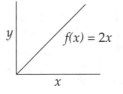

If an economist believes that personal savings results in invest-ment and therefore a strong economy, savings would be the inde-pendent variable—the quantity that causes change. In this case, in-vestment and the economy would be dependent variables, changing in response to variations in personal savings. Another economist might believe that investment leads to more personal savings and therefore a strong economy. Then, investment would be the inde-pendent variable.

ZERO

Multiplying or dividing by zero is a special case. Multiplying by zero will produce an answer of zero. In other words five times nothing is still nothing. Division involving zero is a little more complicated. When the numerator of a fraction equals zero, then the entire fraction equals zero (zero divided by anything is still zero). If, on the other hand, the denominator of a fraction equals zero, the answer is considered "undefined," because there's no meaningful way to divide a quantity by zero. Here are examples:

$$\frac{0}{100} = 0$$

$$\frac{100}{0} = \text{meaningless}$$

THE COMMUTATIVE AND ASSOCIATIVE LAWS

The *commutative and associative laws* for addition and multiplication state that the order of addition or multiplication does not matter:

$$a + b + c = 6, \quad \text{or} \quad a + c + b = 6, \quad \text{or} \quad c + b + a = 6$$

$$a \times b \times c = 6, \quad \text{or} \quad a \times c \times b = 6, \quad \text{or} \quad c \times b \times a = 6$$

REARRANGING EQUATIONS

Using algebraic rules, we can rearrange an equation to solve for unknown quantities. The basic rule for rearranging is that if you add, subtract, multiply, or divide each side of an equation (in different sides of the equal sign) by the same value, the equation will remain true. You can therefore change an equation any way you like, as long as you change both sides together.

Let's rearrange the future value equation to solve for the present value. The basic future value equation is:

$$FV = PV\,(1+i)^n$$

We can reverse the equation, putting present value on the left:

$$PV\,(1+i)^n = FV$$

Then we can divide both sides by the term $(1+i)^n$:

$$\frac{PV\,(1+i)^n}{(1+i)^n} = \frac{FV}{(1+i)^n}$$

We can then cancel the terms $(1+i)^n$ from the left, and get our present value formula:

$$PV = \frac{FV}{(1+i)^n}$$

If you have a fraction in the denominator, like this:

$$\frac{a}{\frac{c}{b}}$$

You can simplify this term through rearrangement. The rule is to bring the fraction from the bottom to the top of the fraction and flip it vertically, resulting in this simplified term:

$$\frac{a \times b}{c}$$

EXPONENTS, ROOTS, AND LOGARITHMS

A number that is multiplied by itself, like $5 \times 5 = 25$, is said to be raised to the power of 2, which is written mathematically like this: 5^2. If a number or expression such as x, is raised to the 4th power, it is written as x^4. The 4 in this term is called an exponent. The opposite of a power or exponent is called the root. Most commonly, we encounter the square root, such as the square root of 25:

$$5 = \sqrt{25}$$

However, just as exponents can be of any power, so can roots. This can be shown either as part of the radical sign or as an fractional exponent. The 3rd root of 27 can be written this way:

$$3 = \sqrt[3]{27} \text{ or } 3 = 27^{\frac{1}{3}}$$

By the way, there's no need to panic if you encounter a negative exponent, as in x^{-3}, it just means one divided by x^3, that is:

$$x^{-3} = \frac{1}{x^3}$$

Terms raised to powers can be multiplied and divided as long as they have the same base. Just follow this rule: Add the exponents when multiplying and subtract them when dividing:

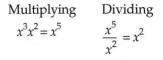

Multiplying   Dividing

$$x^3 x^2 = x^5 \qquad \frac{x^5}{x^2} = x^2$$

If a term with a power is raised to a power itself, then you multiply the exponents:

$$\left(x^3\right)^4 = x^{12}$$

Logarithms may seem a little esoteric, but they are really just another way of writing exponential algebra. Logarithms exist mainly to help us solve an equation to find the value of an exponent, which is trickier than solving for ordinary variables. In the expression $3^3 = 27$, the exponent is known: it's 3. But what if it wasn't known, as in the expression $3^x = 27$? To find the value of x, we can solve the problem directly with logarithms. In chapter 15 on spreadsheets, we'll show you how to solve for the exponent using logarithms. Scientific calculators can also do this type of math for you.

POLYNOMIALS AND MORE TERMS

A *monomial* is a single term, such as $3ax^2$. A *binomial* is an expression having two terms, such as $3ax^2 + 4x$. A *polynomial* is any expression containing two or more terms, such as $3ax^2 + 4x + 6$.

A *linear equation* is one that contains no exponents, like $y = 2x$. A *quadratic equation* is one in which the highest power term is raised to the second power, as in $4x^2 + 3x + 5 = 0$.

When multiplying a monomial, binomial, or polynomial by a certain factor, simply follow the normal multiplication rules, multiplying each term by that factor in turn:

Multiply $(4x + 2)$ by $(x + 3)$

$$
\begin{array}{r}
4x + 2 \\
\underline{x + 3} \\
12x + 6 \quad\longleftarrow\text{ multiply the top expression by 3} \\
\underline{4x^2 + 2x} \quad\longleftarrow\text{ multiply the top expression by } x \\
4x^2 + 14x + 6 \quad\longleftarrow\text{ add the two resultant expressions}
\end{array}
$$

Quadratic equations are common in business math. There are several techniques to solve this type of equation for the unknown (note: quadratic equations usually have two answers, though both won't necessarily make sense). A common method is to factor the equation into two binomials to find the two solutions, which involves a little guesswork:

$$(x + 4)\ (x + 5) = 0$$

To solve a quadratic equation directly, you can also use the quadratic formula. This is the only way to solve quadratic equations when they don't factor neatly. Simply substitute the values from the standard sequence of the quadratic equation, $ax^2 + bx + c$, into this formula:

$$x = \frac{-b \pm \sqrt{b^2 - 4ac}}{2a}$$

INEQUALITIES

To show that an expression is greater than another expression, a greater-than (>) or less-than (<) sign is used. If the expressions could also be equal, then we say "greater-than-or-equal-to" or "less-than-or-equal-to" and draw the symbols this way: $\geq$ and $\leq$.

MATRIX ALGEBRA

Matrix algebra is a powerful method of simultaneously solving many equations with a number of unknowns. A matrix is a rectangular array of numbers in parentheses which represents the coefficients of each equation. The numbers are arranged to form horizontal rows and vertical columns.

Here are two equations which we will solve first with a simple subtraction method, then with matrix algebra.

$$6x + 2y = 14$$
$$2x + y = 5$$

To solve this simple equation by the first method, we multiply the second equation by 2 and get the new second equation:

$$6x + 2y = 14$$
$$4x + 2y = 10$$

Then we simply subtract the second equation from the first, to get:

$$2x + 0 = 4$$

At this point, solving for x is easy: the answer is 2. This is called solving simultaneous equations, and it's very effective when you're working with two equations that are similar in form. However, when many equations and numerous unknowns are involved, this simple method won't do. Matrix algebra comes to the rescue. Let's see how this works using the same set of two equations. First, take the coefficients of the equations and put them into parentheses to form a matrix:

$$\begin{pmatrix} 6 & 2 & 14 \\ 2 & 1 & 5 \end{pmatrix}$$

The rules of matrix algebra allow for changing the second row, as long as we perform the same operation along the entire row. The objective is to get a zero somewhere in the second row of the matrix (just as in the first, simple method.) By inspection, let's multiply the first row by –1 (called R_1) and add 2 to each term in the second row (called R_2). These operations would be designated $-R_1 + 2R_2$. That is, we will multiply the first number in the first row by –1 and then add that to 2 times the first number in row 2:

$$\begin{pmatrix} 6 & 2 & 14 \\ 2 & 1 & 5 \end{pmatrix} \xrightarrow{-R_1 + 2R_2} \begin{pmatrix} 6 & 2 & 14 \\ -2 & 0 & -4 \end{pmatrix}$$

We have now transformed the second row so we have a zero where the y is. We need to reconstruct our equation using the numbers of the second row as coefficients and solve for x, which once again comes out to 2:

$$\begin{aligned} -2x + 0 &= -4 \\ 2x &= 4 \\ x &= 2 \end{aligned}$$

By setting x equal 2 in any of the original equations, we find that y is 1. Equation solved! Although using matrices for this simple problem seems cumbersome, the power of matrices lies in solving many equations at the same time with the computer.

SOLVING PROBLEMS THROUGH ALGEBRA

In chapter 1 on *percentages*, we showed how to determine the resultant investment if you started with $10,000, increased your investment by 100% in the first year and decreased it by 50% in the following year. By performing each calculation separately using a hand-held calculator, we obtained the result of $10,000. We can show this algebraically:

i = investment return each year

$10,000 (1 + i) (1 + i)$

$10,000 (1 + 1) (1 – .5)$

$10,000 (2) (1 – .5)$

$10,000 (1)$

$10,000

Then we described another investment situation, where an initial investment of $50,000 increased by 50% over the first year and decreased 50% over the second year. We obtained the result of $37,500. We can show this algebraically as well:

$50,000 (1 + i) (1 + i)$

$50,000 (1 + .5) (1 - .5)$

$50,000 (1.5) (.5)$

$50,000 (.75)$

$37,500$

In chapter 3 on *ratios,* we discussed P/E ratios and explored a way of finding out a company's earnings using the stock price and P/E ratio published for that company. In a sample problem, we knew from the newspaper the price of a certain company's stock was $82 and its P/E ratio was listed as 26. How to solve for E? Using algebra, we can write the equation and solve:

$$\frac{\text{Price}}{\text{Earnings}} = \text{P/E ratio}$$

$$\frac{P}{E} = P/E \qquad \text{using letters}$$

$$\frac{P}{E} \times E = P/E \times E \qquad \text{multiplying both sides by E}$$

$$P = (P/E)\,E \qquad \text{cancelling E from left side}$$

$$\frac{P}{P/E} = \frac{(P/E)\,E}{P/E} \qquad \text{dividing both sides by P/E}$$

$$\frac{P}{P/E} = E \qquad \text{cancelling P/E from right side}$$

In chapter 5 on *break-even analysis,* we showed how to find a company's break-even point by experimentation. With algebra, however, we can write an equation and solve for the break-even point directly. The example given in chapter 5 involved a company selling units of software for $600 each. Our fixed costs were $600,000, and our variable costs were $100 per unit sold. If we used x as the number of units sold, then our total sales would be $600x$. Our variable costs would be $100x$, and our fixed costs would be $600,000 (fixed costs, remember, don't vary with production). We can add all these quantities together and set them equal to zero in order to find the point at which the company's sales equal its total expenses. The algebraic equation thus formed would be solved this way:

$$600x - (100x + 600{,}000) = 0$$

$$600x - 100x - 600{,}000 = 0$$

$$500x = 600{,}000$$

$$x = 1{,}200$$

Therefore, the break-even point for this company is 1,200 units sold.

APPLICATIONS

Percentages, ratios, and break-even analysis.

10

Interest Rates

Someone once asked me, "How can I tell how much interest I earn?" The trick is that most of the time, there are two different answers. You need to know your interest rate and whether it is simple or compound interest.

Simple interest is a straight calculation. If you invest $1,000 with a bank and it pays 5%, you get $50 at the end of the year. Simple interest is relatively rare these days.

Compound interest involves earning interest on interest during the year. If your $1,000 earns 5% in interest that's compounded monthly, then after one month you've earned $4.16 of interest which is added to your investment. Then, for the next month, you earn interest on $1,004.16. That doesn't look like a whole lot, but it's something. For large amounts of money over long periods, compounding can make a substantial difference.

In this case, instead of earning just 5% with simple interest for the year, you would earn 5.12% with monthly compounded interest. This compound interest is the annual percentage rate that is quoted by the bank.

YIELD VERSUS TOTAL RETURN

Often, when people ask me questions about interest investments, like long-term CDs, stocks or bonds, there appears to be some confusion about what earnings proceed from various investments. When you're thinking about earnings, there are two terms that you should distinguish carefully: *yield* and *total return*.

Yield usually refers to the actual payments you get from investments, like interest from a bank account and dividends from stocks. Yield is the income you receive directly from an investment. Yield is only one component of the benefit you might receive from an investment, however. Some stocks don't pay dividends, but they're still great investments. That's because they *appreciate*, or increase in value over time, so that you can sell them for a profit. To calculate the benefit you receive from an investment, you've got to consider both the yield and the appreciation of that investment. *Total return* includes both yield and appreciation (or depreciation). It's everything you get from an investment. If stocks grow 10% and also *yield* 2% in dividend payments, then the total return from those stocks is 12%.

Above all, the most frequent question I get is, "What investments should I consider?" Most people are concerned with the three most common types of investments: money market funds, bonds, and stocks. These are what people have available in 401(k) or 403(b) plans at work, in mutual funds, or at the friendly neighborhood stock broker.

The yield on money market funds is usually the lowest, although they represent the safest investment type of the three. They evoke the old adage, "no risk, no reward." Bonds pay more, but fluctuate in value in opposition to interest-rate movements. As interest rates increase, bonds decrease in value, and *vice versa*. Stocks pay the least in dividends (regular payments to the investor), but are heavily traded for their potential appreciation in value. The potential appreciation of stocks is their greatest investment value.

In some years, stocks do exceptionally well. In 1995 and 1996, the total returns of the S&P 500 were 37.4% and 23.1%, respectively. On the other hand, in 1994 the total return was only a measly 1.5%, less than a regular savings account might have paid.

At the beginning of 1997, here are the current yields of these three major investment types:

Yield (annual income)

Money market funds 5.0%

Bonds .... 7.5% corporate bonds

Stocks .... 2.0% average dividend

The total return is another matter. In 1996, bonds didn't do particularly well, but stocks had a banner year:

Total Return (yield and appreciation)

Money market funds .... 5.0% (no appreciation)

Bonds .... 1.4% (depreciated in 1996)

Stocks .... 23% (S&P 500 in 1996)

This is not to be taken as an average year. To see stocks appreciate this much in one year is quite unusual.

SUMMARY OF THE THREE INVESTMENTS

Money market investments generally have short maturities. They include money market funds at mutual funds and banks, treasury bills, and CDs and savings accounts at consumer banks. Money market funds also invest in fancier short-term investments like commercial paper and banker's acceptances . Professional investors use money market funds as a parking place for money when they can't decide what to invest in. They're a safe but boring investment.

Bonds, sometimes referred to as fixed-income securities, have longer maturities—as long as 20 or 30 years. Intermediate bonds have terms of 3 to 5 years. In bonds, interest rates are generally higher the longer the maturity. This category includes not only traditional bonds, but also zero-coupon bonds, mortgage-backed securities like Ginnie Maes, and preferred stock which has a fixed dividend. The value of bonds fluctuates in opposition to interest-rate movements.

Stocks, or common stocks, are best known for their daily fluctuations in price. Stocks are pieces of ownership of a corporation. Most investors have no notion of "owning" the company, and are primarily interested in appreciation in stock prices and dividend income, or both.

WHY DO COMPANIES OFFER INTEREST INVESTMENTS ANYWAY?

Let's forget about ourselves as investors for a moment, and look at why companies and financial institutions offer these investments. From economics 101, we know that business needs investments to grow. They can either use funds generated internally, called retained earnings (in other words, they can keep some of their profits to reinvest in the company), or they can go to banks or investors to get money, in order to buy additional machines for production or computers for the office.

Different businesses have different needs, of course, and these investments match those needs. If a company needs short-term funds, for a week or a couple of months, they issue commercial paper, which is bought by money market mutual funds, and you get an annual interest rate (currently around 5%).

But what if a business wants to build a whole new factory? Short-term commercial paper won't do. Bonds will then be the obvious choice. Bonds are issued for many years, corresponding to the time-frame of planning, operating, and making the factory profitable. Companies offer bonds for 15, 20 or more years. Because the company will use investor money for a long time, they have to pay a higher rate of interest. Bonds typically pay interest every six months.

Finally, what if the business just wants to grow in general, hire additional people, rent more office space, increase marketing efforts, and the like? This all costs money. The preferred choice for this type of expense is common stock or, as it is also called, equity financing ("equity" means ownership).

This is where the stock market comes in. If the market does well, as it has for the past two years, companies can issue more stock, or smaller companies can "go public" through an initial public offering (IPO), in which they sell a portion of the company to investors in the form of stock. However, if the market is down, companies are discouraged, because their ability to raise money would be greatly diminished. At worst, the market might actually reject additional stock.

Dividends are usually paid out to investors of common stock, except for smaller companies which have not reached stability to do so on a regular basis. Dividends are usually paid quarterly. Once dividends are paid out, investors tend to expect them regularly. Therefore, companies think long and hard about their dividend policy. Generally, dividends don't change very much. If investors are to receive $1 in dividends for the year, that's probably what they're going to receive for a number of years in the future. If earnings warrant increasing the dividends, companies may increase them, cautiously.

DOES THE FED CONTROL INTEREST RATES?

Yes, the Fed controls short-term interest rates. No, it does not control long-term rates directly.

Through monetary policy, the Federal Reserve (Fed) controls short-term interest rates directly, by setting inter-bank loan interest rates and selling or buying treasury issues. These actions are attempts not only to control interest rates, but also to fine-tune the economy. If the economy appears to be getting stronger, the Fed will increase interest rates in hopes of slowing the economy down. In the same way, if the economy looks like it is slowing down too much, then the Fed will decrease rates in hopes of spurring the economy. The objective of the Fed is admirable—to keep the economy growing steadily without any recessions.

Long-term interest rates, unlike short-term rates, fluctuate primarily according to overall expectations of inflation. Collectively, if you and I believe that inflation is low and will probably remain low, then we are less likely to ask for hefty raises, and will tend not to tolerate price increases in grocery stores and elsewhere. Importantly, we also will not demand higher long-term interest rates. If, on the other hand, we collectively expect inflation to kick up, we'll ask for higher raises, tolerate higher prices for oranges, and demand higher long-term interest rates.

If the Fed can keep the economy on an even keel, then inflation will remain moderate, and long-term interest rates will remain under control as well. In this way the Fed exercises indirect control over long-term interest rates.

THE COMPONENT MODEL OF INTEREST RATES

Now we come to one of the two most fascinating topics regarding interest: *The structure of interest rates.* The other topic—*the capital asset pricing model*—will be dealt with shortly.

Understanding the structure of interest rates involves looking at the relationships between inflation, short- and long-term interest rates, and the stock market itself. We do this through the component model.

We start by looking at the relationship between inflation and money market rates to give us what is called real interest rates:

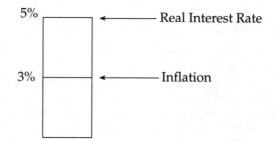

Real interest rates at the moment are about 2%, because short-term rates are earning about 5% and inflation is about 3%. Historically, short-term rates only earn about 1% above inflation, all things being equal. Thus, with inflation at about 3%, money market rates "should" be about 4% on the basis of their historical relationship.

Since actual short-term rates at the moment are about 5%, we are getting an unusually large amount of interest, according to this model. We could speculate that the Fed doesn't want the economy to heat up too much, and is therefore purposely keeping short rates a little on the high side.

In discussing these interest rates, it might be best to repeat two terms introduced in chapter 4: *nominal* and *real* interest rates. Nominal means the actual or official rate, whereas real means the rate adjusted for compounding and inflation. In this example, 5% would be the nominal rate, whereas 2% would be the real rate.

Next, we add long-term treasury rates to our model:

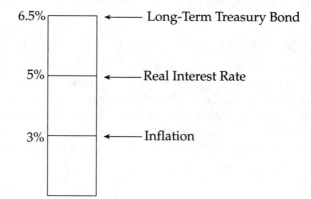

Historically, long-term treasury bonds earn rates about 1.5% above short-term treasury issues. This is sometimes called the horizon rate. Corporate long-term bonds are usually another 1% above treasury rates. Corporate bonds entail some risk, whereas theoretically treasuries have none. Thus, we can add long-term corporate bonds to our model:

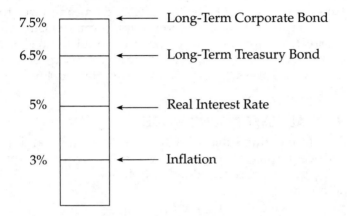

To complete the model, we can include the historical additional return stocks give, which is about 4.5%:

Component Model

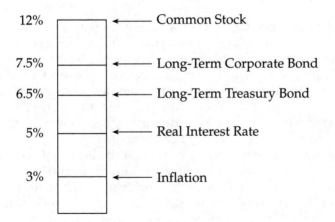

The technical term for the difference between long-term rates and the stock market total return is *equity premium*. A premium is an additional cost or benefit. Historically, you should be able to earn an additional 4.5% return with equity, or common stock.

Our model is now complete. It allows us to answer a number of questions, based on these historical relationships. Question: Are long- term treasury issues too high or low? Answer: A teensy bit high; if money rates should be about 4%, then long-term treasury rates should be about 5.5%. Question: If long-term treasury rates are indeed correct, then what kind of return should I expect from the stock market? Answer: About 12%. If treasury rates are 6.5% and are about right (who knows?), add 1% for corporate and 4.5% for stocks to get 12%.

CAPM: CAPITAL ASSET PRICING MODEL

The second fascinating subject involving interest rates and the stock market is a centerpiece of modern investment theory. It's the *capital asset pricing model*, abbreviated as CAPM.

In the formula:

$$R = r_f + \beta \left(r_m - r_f \right)$$

R is the return

r_f is the risk-free return

r_m is the market rate return

β is beta, or its riskiness

This formula can be used in a variety of ways, but for our purposes here, we can relate it to an investor's or company's targeted investment return. Consequently, R represents the *return* that is sought from investments. From an investor's perspective, the *return* means the total return you reap from an investment. From a company's perspective, the return is often the hurdle or cost of capital that you will use in judging projects and other business ventures through present-value calculations.

In the formula, beta (sometimes called the beta coefficient) represents a common stock's volatility versus the overall stock market (volatility is the degree to which a stock's price fluctuates). The S&P 500 index, which is usually used to represent the stock market as a whole, historically has a standard deviation of about 20.5%. That's the annual variation of the market in general. If an individual stock matches this variation, it is said to have a beta of 1. If its variation is 10% wider than the S&P 500's, it's said to have a beta of 1.1. A stock that varies 10% less than the market has a beta of 0.9.

The last two variables in the formula, r_f and r_m, refer to the return of a risk-free investment, which is most often represented by short-term treasury bills, and the return of the stock market, which is represented by the return of the S&P 500. Knowing these values, you're ready to solve the formula for your company.

Let's say your company's stock has a beta of 1.2, the treasury bill rate is currently 5%, and the long-term market return is estimated at 12%. After we enter these values into the formula we obtain our required return of 13.4%:

$$R = .05 + 1.2 \ (.12 - .05) = 13.4\%$$

From a technical point-of-view, this 13.4% represents the investment return we should expect from a stock that has this volatility when the stock market's return is around 12%. We should expect an additional return for our higher volatility stock—in this case 1.4% higher. We recall the old adage of higher risk, higher return. Individual investors use this formula in selecting individual stocks as well as mutual funds.

There is a caveat to be heeded when using this formula. In recent years, the concept of beta has come into question. In analyzing the beta of individual stocks and mutual funds, it is found that beta can change, and in some cases change significantly. (Beta is usually calculated using data from the past three years.) Thus, if beta itself varies, then how reliable is the result of the formula at given point?

LOANS AND LEASES

Interest rates, as you might suspect, play an important role in money you have to pay credit cards, banks, and car dealers for the use of their money. In these cases, they're the investors, and you're the investee, so to speak.

You are typically charged a monthly interest rate for whatever is left of the outstanding loan, as with credit cards. Paying only the minimum amount that is allowed by the cards, as you might have gathered, is not the best of strategies. At rates at 18% or so, if you only paid the minimum amount, you could be paying off that credit card well into your retirement years.

For car leases, you must often pay a slightly higher interest rate than if you purchased the car with a loan from the car dealer. However important the precise interest rate is, and it is important, there may be greater considerations involved in leases. You might, for example, tend to drive a car more than the lease normally permits, thus increasing the cost of the lease far more than a slightly higher interest rate.

If a loan is amortized, which is quite common, that means you pay an equal amount each month, but the component of interest varies, with most of your monthly payment going to interest early on, and less later. Ask for a schedule of monthly interest and principal to be paid. It allows you see the value of paying off these loans quickly, if financially possible.

TAXABLE VERSUS TAX-FREE MUNICIPAL INTEREST

To review the rules: municipal-bond interest is generally tax-exempt on your federal tax return, and if the bonds are from your state then this income is generally exempt from your state income taxes. If I bought New York bonds, they would not be exempt from my New Jersey tax return.

In your personal investments, to the extent that you are invested in interest-bearing investments, should you invest in taxable bonds or tax-free municipal ones? The answer: It depends on your marginal tax bracket. That's the tax bracket your income tops out in. The highest brackets are 36% and 39.6% at the moment. The quick answer is that if you're in these high brackets, then you should invest in municipal tax-free investments. If you're in the lowly 15% bracket you should invest in fully taxable investments. If you're in the middle brackets, 28% and 31%, like most of us, it's an even calculation. It doesn't make much difference.

Here's how to do the calculation. Assume that you could earn taxable interest at a rate of 7.5% or tax-free interest at a rate of 5%. The question to ask yourself is, "How much do I get to keep?". If you're in the 36% bracket, you get to keep 64%. The government gets to keep 36%, because in your tax bracket any additional income is taxed at a rate of 36%. If the taxable interest is 7.5%, simply multiply it by 64% to get 4.8%. That's your bottom line, the share you get to keep. Since the tax-free interest rate is 5% in our example, then tax-free investments would be a little more profitable for you.

It's helpful simply to ask yourself what you get to keep, instead of doing elaborate calculations on paper. After a moment, people can usually do this math in their heads. Technically, you're actually subtracting your investment's marginal tax bracket from 100% to find the percentage of new income that you get to keep:

$$100\% - \frac{\text{marginal}}{\text{tax bracket}} = \frac{\text{what you}}{\text{keep}}$$

$$100\% - 36\% = 64\%$$

To be precise, the calculation should include state income taxes, except in a few states like Florida and Texas that have no income tax. If you don't itemize deductions, then you simply add the two marginal taxes together. However, if you do itemize deductions, then you take off on your federal what you pay on your state tax. Your state income tax is a deduction on your federal return.

Assume again that you're in the 36% federal bracket (meaning that you keep 64% of any new income). If you're paying 5% in state tax, then you end up paying only 64% of 5%, or 3.2%. You get to save 36% of your state tax, or in this case you've saved 1.8% through federal deductions:

If you're in the 36% federal tax bracket

If you're in a 5% state tax bracket

$$5\% \times 64\% = 3.2\%$$

RULE: YOU SAVE YOUR TAX BRACKET

Sometimes it's hard to see what you save by taking a tax deduction. For instance, if you give a $100 tax-deductible gift to a non-profit charity, you are actually saving your tax bracket. If you itemize deductions, and you are in the 28% bracket, then you save 28% of $100, or $28.

INTEREST RATES IN PERSPECTIVE

As interesting as they are, interest rates also play a crucial role in calculating some of the more important quantities used in business math: present and future value. These are taken up in the next chapter.

11

Present and Future Value

Present and future value calculations start with the simple formula:

$$FV = PV(1 + i)^n$$

The letters represent the following:

FV is future value

PV is present value

i is interest

n is the number of years

You may see other letters for this formula. For instance, sometimes r is used for rate of interest and t for time, but rest assured, the actual letters make no difference.

If you have $10 today and it earns 8% for 4 years, then you end up with $13.60:

$$FV = \$10(1 + .00)^4$$
$$FV = \$13.60$$

Believe it or not, you can actually use a simple hand-held calculator to do this calculation. Enter 1.08 and multiply by 1.08 to get 1.1664. If you continue to press the = key (on most calculators), you will be multiplying by 1.08 again and again. In this case, if you press the = key a total of 3 times you will get 1.3604. Then, multiply by 10 to get $13.60. (You only need to press the = key 3 times, because the first time already multiplies 1.08 twice.)

If your money is compounded more frequently than once a year, then you can insert another variable, x, to account for it:

$$FV = PV(1 + \frac{i}{x})^{(n + x)}$$

We divide the interest rate by 12 and multiply the period by 12. Thus, if the money is compounded monthly, you divide the interest rate by 12 and multiply the period by 12:

$$FV = \$10(1 + \frac{.08}{12})^{(4 \times 12)}$$

$$FV = \$13.76$$

To do this with a simple calculator, first divide .08 (your yearly interest rate) by 12 to get .00666 (your monthly interest rate), and add one to get 1.00666. Press the M+ key to save this value. Press the multiply key, and press the MC (memory recall) key, then press the = key to get 1.0133. You have now multiplied the precise value twice. Press the = key 46 more times to get 1.37566. Multiply by 10 to get the answer of $13.76.

BUT SHOULDN'T I FIGURE TAXES INTO THESE CALCULATIONS?

The answer is yes, and no. Yes, you do want to identify the taxes you pay on investments. You may even decide to invest in tax-free municipal bonds because of your taxes, as discussed in the last chapter on interest rates.

No, because in most cases you will not actually pay taxes from each of your investments. For instance, I've never known a person who goes to each investment he has, calculates the actual taxes for that investment, and removes that amount from each investment. Instead, you leave all the money in your investments and pay your taxes from your other pocket. That is, you do pay taxes, but not from the actual investments. People often have one particular account from which taxes are paid. Thus, if your CD at your bank pays 8%, use that percentage to project your money. At the same time, remember that there are taxes to be paid and that you need to set aside money to pay them.

PRESENT VALUE

Using simple algebra rules, we can rearrange our basic formula and solve for the present value. (Chapter 9, on algebra, details this rearrangement.) Here's our newly rearranged equation for present value:

$$PV = \frac{FV}{(1+i)^n}$$

For instance, if you wanted to have $1,000 in five years (future value) and your money could earn 5%, you can insert the values and get the present value of $783.53. This is how much you would need to invest today—the present value of $1,000 five years from now.

$$PV = \frac{\$1,000}{(1+.05)^s}$$

To do this with a simple calculator, first multiply 1.05 by 1.05 to get 1.1025. Press the = key 3 more times to get 1.2762. Press the M+ key to save the answer. Enter $1,000, press the divide key, press the MC (memory recall) key, then press the = key to get the answer of $783.53.

By the way, the interest rate in present value calculations is often called the *discount rate*. This refers to the fact that the present value is less than future value. It's a discounted value.

Up to this point, we have dealt with simple present and future values—a single amount of money invested today growing to a future value. Or, vice versa, a present value calculated from a single future value. The real world is often more complicated that this.

PRESENT AND FUTURE VALUE OF ANNUITIES

Here we are dealing with a series of payments, which are called *annuities* in math circles. Examples are pensions or Social Security, in which retirees receive monthly payments for the rest of their lives. Some companies even call their pensions *annuity plans,*and their pensioners *annuitants.*

The word *annuity* comes from Latin, meaning annual. It means the payment of an equal amount of money for a certain length of time. Sometimes, as with pensions, it is for the remainder of someone's life. Actuaries calculate the average life expectancy for everyone, so the pension plan can at least plan for people living their average life expectancies, and can calculate how much money it needs.

Annuities can work both ways. They can represent not only payments to you, but also a contribution from you into an investment, such as your adding money into your 401(k) or 403(b) plans at work. Thus, an annuity is a series of equal payments to or from you.

The following is a diagram of an annuity plan:

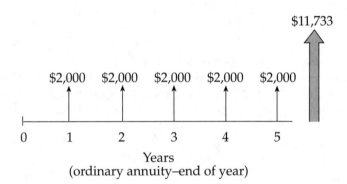

Years
(ordinary annuity–end of year)

It shows contributions of $2,000 made each year, say, to an IRA. It also shows that the contributions are made at the end of each year.

Contributions made at the end of the year are called *ordinary annuities*, in contrast to an *annuity due*, in which contributions are made at the beginning of each year.

In this example, an annuity due would have netted you about 8% more (8% interest). That's an extra $1,000 over the ordinary annuity. $12,671 versus $11,733. Each contribution works for you all during the year and pays off for you.

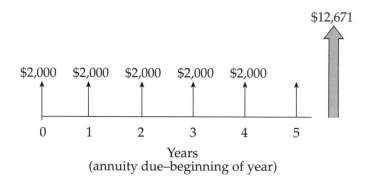

$12,671

$2,000 $2,000 $2,000 $2,000 $2,000

0   1   2   3   4   5

Years
(annuity due–beginning of year)

The actual formula for the future value of an ordinary annuity is:

Future Value of an Ordinary Annuity (end of year)

$$FV = Pmt \ \frac{(1+i)^n - 1}{i}$$

"Pmt" stands for payment. That's the amount of each annuity payment.

For instance, we can calculate the value of our IRA after five years as:

$$FV = \$2,000 \ \frac{(1+.08)^5 - 1}{i}$$

$$FV = \$11,733$$

And yes, you can actually use a simple calculator to perform this calculation. Enter 1.08 and multiply by 1.08 to get 1.1664. If you continue to press the = key (on most calculators) you will be multiplying by 1.08 again and again. In this case, if you press the = key a total of 4 times you will get 1.469. Then, subtract 1, and divide by .08 to get 5.8666. Finally, multiply this percentage by $2,000 to get the value of this annuity after five years, $11,733.

The future value of an annuity due is:

Future Value of an Annuity Due (beginning of year)

$$FV = Pmt \ \frac{(1+i)^{n+1} - 1}{i} - 1$$

Inserting the amount of our IRA contribution, we can calculate our answer, $12,671:

$$FV = \$2,000 \ \frac{(1+.08)^{5+1} - 1}{i} - 1$$

$$FV = \$12,671$$

Using algebra, we can rearrange the future value formulas for *present value*:

Present Value of an Ordinary Annuity (end of year)

$$PV = Pmt \ \frac{1 - \dfrac{1}{1+i}}{i}^{n-2} + 1$$

Present Value of an Annuity Due (beginning of year)

$$PV = Pmt \ \frac{1 - \dfrac{1}{1+i^n}}{i} + 1$$

Sometimes, as with some commercial annuities, or with social security as it's currently constructed, annuity payments can increase each year, in what could be best described as increasing annuities.

AN INCREASING ANNUITY

The most common example of an increasing annuity is your contributions to your 401(k) or 403(b) plan. Hopefully, you receive salary increases, so your contributions (which are calculated as a percentage of your salary) automatically increase as well. If your salary is $35,000 and you contribute 6% to your 401(k) plan, your annual contribution is $2,100. If you get a 5% salary increase to $36,750, then 6% of your new salary is $2,205. Of course, your company's contributions should also increase.

To calculate this valuable 401(k) projection, you will have to use a software package that allows for increasing annuities.

LOOKING BEHIND THE SCENES AT CONSTRUCTING A MAGAZINE TABLE

For the past 15 years, I've constructed many tables, worksheets, and checked many calculations for major publications, including the *Wall Street Journal*, *Fortune*, and *Money* magazine.

Recently, I completed a worksheet for a newsletter *Money* magazine publishes to calculate the future value of your 401(k). The newsletter is scheduled to appear the spring of 1997 in the "Money Financial Guidance Series: In Your Prime," will deal specially with the issue of how to handle a retirement payout.

The worksheet is as follows:

Worksheet

	Example	Yours
1. Value of 401(k) now	10,000	
2. Factor from Table A	4.66	
3. Multiply lines 1 and 2:	46,600	
4. Your annual contributions	2,800	
5. Your company's contributions	1,050	
6. TOTAL lines 4 and 5	3,850	
7. Factor from Table B	57.10	
8. Multiply lines 6 and 7:	219,835	
9. Add lines 3 and 8:	266,435	

Estimated investment earnings

		5%	8%	12%
	5	1.28	1.47	1.76
Table A	10	1.63	2.16	3.11
	15	2.08	3.17	5.47
	20	2.65	(4.66)	9.65

	Salary increases		Salary increases		Salary increases	
5	5.53	0%	5.87	0%	6.35	0%
	5.85	3%	6.20	3%	6.70	3%
	6.08	5%	6.43	5%	6.94	5%
Table B 10	12.58	0%	14.49	0%	17.55	0%
	14.25	3%	16.30	3%	19.58	3%
	15.51	5%	17.67	5%	21.10	5%
15	21.58	0%	27.15	0%	37.28	0%
	26.05	3%	32.28	3%	43.51	3%
	29.70	5%	36.44	5%	48.49	5%
20	33.07	0%	45.76	0%	72.05	0%
	42.36	3%	57.10	3%	87.11	3%
	50.54	5%	66.92	5%	99.90	5%

The only instructions from the *Money* editors were to put together an easy-to-use worksheet to help people to calculate the future value of their 401(k) plans. I sketched out a minimalist worksheet, including only what was necessary: starting balance and current contributions. But how to account for increases in contributions?

I constructed what could be called a three-dimensional table in two dimensions. It accounted for 0%, 3%, and 5% salary increases. A salary increase of zero percent was included for two reasons. First, people often do conservative planning, preferring to first calculate the value of their retirement package assuming no salary increases. Secondly, people in many companies find salary increases both infrequent and small, so that a 0% raise could be close to reality.

I also decided to separate the current balance from the contributions. Not only would this make the math easier, it would also potentially give the reader the ability to use the worksheet and tables in a creative way. For instance, a reader may not be contributing to their plan temporarily because of personal financial problems.

Let's say that a reader was looking for a job, and had rolled over the 401(k) balance from his previous job into an IRA. The reader could speculate that if a job had a one-year waiting period to start a new 401(k), then the reader could project the values of both the IRA and new 401(k) separately.

By the way, if you have a loan outstanding on your 401(k), and your loan rate is similar to what your investments are earning, then you can assume for calculation purposes that you don't have a loan and all the money is still in the plan. You are paying yourself back at the about the same rate as your investments are earning. Your inflow and outflow are equal.

NET PRESENT VALUE

Continuing our discussion of present and future value, there is a common business concept called *net present value*. It's the present value of an uneven stream of payments. Often in a business project, there are proposed cash flows (generally uneven) and management wants to know the present value of those cash flows. Real estate projects and new business ventures typically have estimated and varying annual cash flows, sometimes negative but hopefully mostly positive. Net present value can be represented as:

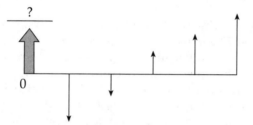

You could, of course, find the present value of each cash flow by discounting each and adding up all the present values. But computer spreadsheets, and scientific calculators, have this calculation built in. You can enter your cash flow values and calculate present value with the touch of a button.

WHAT DISCOUNT RATE TO USE?

Normally, the discount rate used to calculate present value is the rate of return you, or your company, would earn if you took all the money earmarked for your project and invested it instead. This is sometimes called the *internal rate of return* (IRR). It's the rate your money would earn if invested in financial assets. At large companies, this is often casually referred to as the *hurdle rate*, or more technically, the *cost of capital*. To many financial analysts, it's known as the IRR. Since you can earn that rate outside the company, it's the rate against which you judge internal projects.

As an example, let's say that the following were the cash flows for a project and the discount, IRR, rate was 12%:

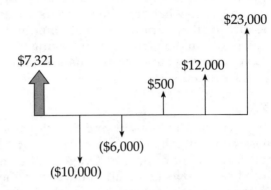

In chapter 15, on spreadsheets, we'll show you how to use the NPV math function that is built into spreadsheets. Doing so would automatically give us the answer, which is $7,321. You could also calculate the present value of each payment, then add them together.

Interestingly, if the discount rate were only 8%, the present value would be $10,467, versus the present value of $7,321 calculated using a rate of 12%. A lower interest rate gives a higher present value. Why? Because the lower the discount, or hurdle, rate, the more money you would need to overcome a lower return. If the interest rate is higher, then you're projecting that your money will be growing faster, which means you need less money now to achieve a certain amount later.

In this process, negative as well as positive values are combined. A caution, however: Usually, if there are more than two sign changes in the series of cash flows, the answer is likely to be uncertain or incorrect using most spreadsheets or scientific calculators. In those cases, you may want to verify your answer by calculating the positive and negative cash flows separately and then adding them together, just to make sure.

YOUR MORTGAGE IS AN ANNUITY

If you solve for the payment size (pmt) in the formula for the present value of an annuity with a monthly interest rate, then you're calculating your monthly mortgage payment.

Your mortgage is also known as an *amortized* loan. That's a loan that requires an equal payment each month that includes some interest and some principal. The initial payments are mostly interest, and the last payments mostly principal.

A diagram of your typical fixed-rate, thirty-year mortgage looks like this:

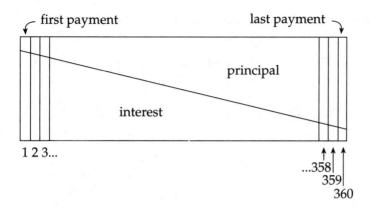

first payment   last payment

principal

interest

1 2 3...

...358
359
360

Mathematically, as we've seen, a mortgage is an ordinary annuity calculation with monthly interest. Adjusting for monthly payments, the formula for your mortgage payment is:

$$Pmt = \frac{PV}{1 - \dfrac{1}{\left(1 + \dfrac{i}{12}\right) n \times 12}}$$

Where i is the interest rate that you're quoted from the bank or mortgage company, and n is the number of years the mortgage will run—30, 20, 15, or whatever.

If you are unfamiliar with spreadsheets, check out chapter 15, where we'll show you how to use spreadsheet math functions.

SUMMARY OF THE BASIC FORMULAS

Here are the basic formulas used in this chapter, including the simplified present value of annuities:

Future Value:

$$FV = PV(1 + i)^n$$

Present Value:

$$PV = \frac{FV}{(1 + i)^n}$$

Future Value of an Ordinary Annuity (end of year):

$$PV = Pmt \frac{(1 + i)^n - 1}{i}$$

Future Value of an Annuity Due (beginning of year):

$$FV = Pmt\left(\frac{(1+i)^{n+1}-1}{i}-1\right)$$

Present Value of an Ordinary Annuity (end of year):

$$PV = Pmt\,\frac{1-\dfrac{1}{(1+i)^n}}{i}$$

Present Value of an Annuity Due (beginning of year):

$$PV = Pmt\,\frac{1-\dfrac{1}{(1+i)^{n-1}}}{i}+1$$

APPLICATIONS

401(k), IRAs, and mortgages.

CHAPTER 12

Statistics:
The Basics

There are several universal "truths" expressed mathematically that we use in business. There is the 80-20 rule that says that 80% of the company's earnings are produced by only 20% of its products or services. There is the S-shaped curve that parallels how a product is accepted in the marketplace, or how we learn new procedures. There are logarithms that duplicate growth, such as growth of the population. But, the granddaddy of them all is the bell-shaped curve, which is at the core of statistics.

The word *statistics* has two meanings. It can mean the whole body of techniques and mathematical methods used to collect, analyze, and present information. This chapter and the next two deal generally with the subjects included in the field of statistics. It can also mean a specific group of numerical values, such as the mean or standard deviation of a group of numbers. A statistician, is one who uses mathematics to interpret numerical information.

The mathematics of statistics appears to have started in the late 1700s in London and was described by the word "statist," an old word for statesman or politician. Many mathematical or statistical methods of interpretation have developed since then. The world of economics and finance relies on statistics. Today, businesses routinely use statistics in manufacturing, distribution, marketing, and sales, and in the operation of various departments such as accounting, purchasing, and human resources.

EXAMPLE: TOO MANY DEFECTS

You, as an engineer, have been told to study the number of defects at plant A. You tested 100 products each day for 16 days and recorded the number of defects you found. You listed the information two ways, chronologically and by number of defects:

day	number of defects	number of defects	frequency occurred
1	15	11	1
2	18	12	
3	20	13	1
4	13	14	1
5	17	15	1
6	11	16	1
7	19	17	1
8	21	18	3
9	18	19	2
10	16	20	2
11	20	21	1
12	18	22	1
13	24	23	
14	19	24	1
15	14	25	
16	22	26	

As a highly trained engineer, you know that you can plot this information on either a histogram or a stem-and-leaf diagram.

HISTOGRAM—A BAR CHART IN DISGUISE

A *histogram* is a simple frequency diagram. It's one of the basic ways to represent statistical data. Although it looks like a bar chart (which it is), it's called a histogram. It comes from the Greek word *histos* for mast, because of its mast-like columns. A histogram's bars represent the frequencies with which certain values occur within a sample.

Using your keen engineering skills, you grouped the data and constructed a histogram of the defects found at Plant A:

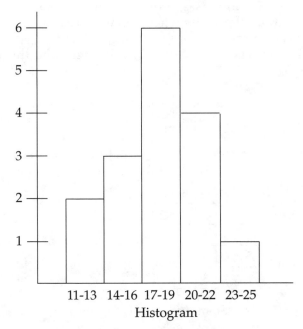

Histogram

If you create too many columns, you may not get a good visual of the data; if you create too few, you'll lose perspective. By trial and error, you can obtain the right number of columns to give a useful visual look at the information. In most cases, between 4 and 20 groupings usually seems right.

For the mathematically minded, there's a suggested formula to estimate how many data groupings, or bars, you might try:

$$g = 1 + 3.3 \log n$$

Where g is the *number of groups*, or bars, and n is *the number of observations* in your sample.

So, if you have 16 observations, you might try 5 groupings:

$$g = 1 + 3.3 \log (15)$$

$$g = 1 + 3.3 \ (1.2)$$

$$g = 4.96$$

A STEM-AND-LEAF DIAGRAM

To me it looks like an ancient Chinese puzzle, but it's called *stem-and-leaf*. It can, in many cases, provide a quick visual representation of the information, especially when you want to compare two sets of data. However, in our case, it seems appropriate.

Checking your statistics textbook, you might find this example:

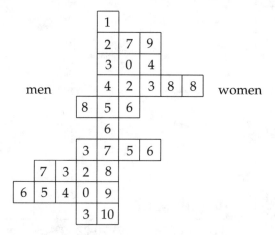

Stem–and–Leaf Diagram

It shows the number of minutes men and women spent watching sports during a particular week. The stem and leaf diagram in this example provides a quick visual demonstration of the difference between men and women. Each participant's number of minutes were noted on the stem-and-leaf diagram. For instance, the shortest times for women were 27 and 29, and the longest times were 75 and 76. The stem in this case represents 10 minutes. The leaf is just a block to the right or left, with the second digit noted. All blocks are the same size. For men, you can see that the shortest time was 58 minutes, and the maximum time was 103 minutes.

THE BELL-SHAPED CURVE—THE CENTRAL DIAGRAM OF STATISTICS

In statistics, the *bell-shaped curve* is at the center of mathematics. It represents the real-world frequency of many phenomena in business, science, and our daily lives. It represents the variations in product quality measured by quality control departments; it represents the demographics of our customers; and it represents common responses to surveys. To the extent that products, customers, and surveys do not conform to the bell curve, we can then describe the events relative to that nonconformity.

The bell-shaped curve or bell curve, is also variously called the *normal curve*, the *normal distribution*, or the *frequency distribution*. Technically, it's known as a *Gaussian curve* or *distribution*, from the mathematician Karl Gauss (1777-1855).

Before we go much further, here's the curve in question:

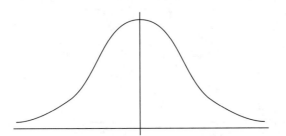

Bell–shaped Curve

It is also correctly called the *ideal* or *symmetrical distribution curve*, implying that the real world is often a little different from the pure curve itself. In the real business world, observations may vary from this standard curve. Real-world distribution curves may have higher or lower peaks, as shown here:

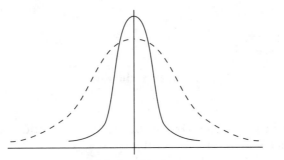

Higher Peak

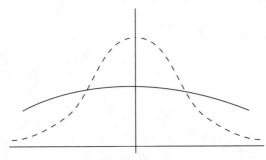

Lower Peak

A real-world distribution curve may also not be centered, in which case it's considered "skewed":

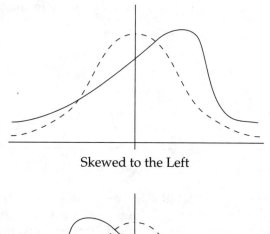

Skewed to the Left

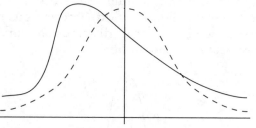

Skewed to the Right

We generally characterize all of these distributions by their central tendencies or their variability:

- central tendencies: mean (average), median, and mode
- variability: range, variance, and standard deviation

CENTRAL TENDENCIES

In a normal curve, the mean, median, and mode are all the same. It is when the curve is skewed that these three measurements are different.

The *mean*, often called the average or arithmetic mean, is the value obtained by adding all the values and dividing by the number of values. It is the most common of all statistical measurements. It's often represented in statistical formulas by *x*-bar, or a bar over an *x*:

the mean:

$$\bar{x} = \frac{x_1 + x_2 + \dots + x_n}{n}$$

The n in the equation is the number of values or observations. The mean of 4, 8, 8, 17, 23 is 12.

$$\bar{x} = \frac{4 + 8 + 8 + 17 + 23}{5}$$

$$\bar{x} = 12$$

The *median* is the midpoint of the data values. It's the number in the middle when the numbers are in order. Just like the highway "median strip" divides the road into equal halves, the median divides the set of values. The median of the following numbers: 4, 8, 8, 17, 23 is 8. If there's an *even* number of values, then the median is the average of the two middle values. For instance, the median of the following four numbers.5: 4, 8, 17, 23 is 12 (because 8 + 17 equals 25, divided by 2, equals 12.5).

The *mode* is the most common data value. The mode of the following numbers: 4, 8, 8, 17, 23 is 8.

SKEWNESS AND THE MEAN, MEDIAN, AND MODE

A distribution that is not symmetrical is said to be skewed; it tilts to one side or another. If the distribution is completely symmetrical, then the mean, mode and median are the same and the skewness would be zero.

The distribution is said to be skewed to the right when the mean is to the right, or greater, than the mode. That is, the peak of the distribution is toward the left (which may seem counter intuitive).

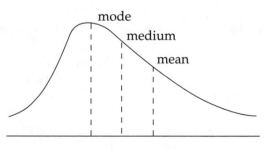

Skewed to the Right

The distribution is skewed to the left when the mean is to the left, or less than, the mode and the curve appears to "lean" to the right.

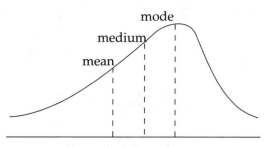

Skewed to the Left

VARIABILITY

A normal curve looks somewhat like a bell—hence the name. (Although it always seemed to me like a pretty flat-looking bell. Our Liberty Bell in Philadelphia—now *there's* a bell shape.)

If the curve is flatter or steeper than a normal curve, it's usually just referred to as a steep or flat curve. In statistics, this quality of flatness or steepness is called the *peakedness* of the curve, or, even more technically, the curve's *kurtosis*.

The *range* is a measure of how dispersed a distribution is. It's the difference between the maximum and minimum values in the distribution. An *outlier* is a very small or very large value that's far removed from most of the other values.

The *variance* is a measure of dispersion of all the values together. It is based on the difference between each value and the mean:

Variance:

$$\sigma = \Sigma \frac{\left(x_i - \overline{x}\right)^2}{n}$$

Where σ^2 is the variance, x_i represents each value, n is the number of values.

The quantity is squared in the formula so that negative differences don't cancel positive differences. We're looking for the magnitude of the differences.

The *standard deviation* is the square root of the variance, and usually represents the most important description of the dispersion of a population or sample:

standard deviation:

$$\sigma = \sqrt{\Sigma \frac{\left(x_i - \bar{x}\right)^2}{n}}$$

Where σ is the standard deviation.

The small Greek letter sigma, σ, is used to represent standard deviation. Standard deviation measures how data values are spread around the mean, or average, of a data sample. Also, the standard deviation is in the same units as the data. For instance, if the data are in dollars, the standard deviation will be in dollars as well.

One standard deviation is approximately 68%, about two-thirds, of the data values. Or, put another way, we generally expect that two-thirds of our data will fall within one standard deviation of the mean. Two standard deviations capture approximately 95% of the data. Three standard deviations capture approximately 99% of the data. Four sigma, or four standard deviations, specifies 99.9521% of all values.

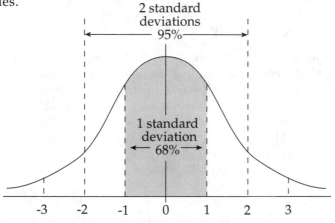

Standard Deviations

In quality circles, the term *six sigma* is commonly used. It represents the highest standard in quality control, specifying that there should be no more than 3.4 errors per million. Six standard deviations includes 99.99976% of all the data values.

The standard deviation of the numbers 4, 8, 8, 17, and 23 is 6.96. We already calculated the mean to be 12. Here's the standard deviation calculation:

$\bar{x}=12$ (mean)		
x_i	$12-x_i$	$(12-x_i)^2$
4	8	64
8	4	16
8	4	16
17	-5	25
23	-11	121
		242

$$\frac{242}{5} = 48.4$$

$$\sqrt{48.4} = \underline{\underline{6.96}}$$

WHAT'S YOUR Z SCORE?

It's the handy measurement of the number of standard deviations. A z score of 2 means it is 2 standard deviations from the mean, or average. A z score of 3.5 is three-and-a-half standard deviations. This leads us to discuss the area of the bell curve.

AREA UNDER THE CURVE

We now can enter deeper into the world of statistics. Since we have established the concepts of mean and standard deviation, then we can start to examine the bell curve in a more fundamental way. The first step is to understand that the area below the curve represents all of the possible events or observations to be considered, for whatever we are studying. Those events in the center are more likely to happen, which is why the curve is so tall there. All the events within one standard deviation will be 68% of all events. Two deviations, 95%, and so on.

The entire area under the curve is therefore 100% of all the value in the sample; collectively, these events have a probability of 1 (if something is certain, 100% sure, then we say it has a probability of 1).

Using the nomenclature of z scores, we can then represent any portion of the curve with the table:

Area under the Curve

z	.00	.01	.02	.03	.04
0.0	.0000	.0040	.0080	.0120	.0160
0.1	.0398	.0438	.0478	.0517	.0557
0.2	.0793	.0832	.0871	.0910	.0948
0.3	.1179	.1217	.1255	.1293	.1331
0.4	.1554	.1591	.1628	.1664	.1700
0.5	.1915	.1950	.1985	.2019	.2054
0.6	.2257	.2291			
0.7	.2580	.2612			
0.8	.2881	.2910			
0.9	.3159	.3186			
1.0	(.3413)	.3438			
1.1	.3643	.3665			
1.2	.3849	.3869			
1.3	.4032	.4049			

If you wanted to find the area under the curve for 1 standard deviation (values with a z score of 1), you would find an area of .3413. That, however, is only one half of the area, to the right of the midpoint. You would need to add the other half—another .3413—to get the full area of 1 standard deviation, which is .6826, or in percentage terms, 68.26%. The full table appears at the end of this chapter.

DOES A CAMEL HAVE ONE OR TWO HUMPS?

In statistics, real-world events don't always fit the standard curve neatly. A *bimodal distribution* is a distribution where there are two peaks, or modes, of data, versus the typical single peak.

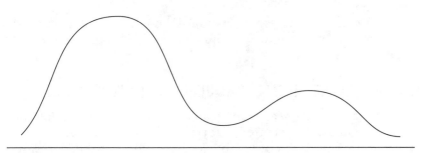

Bimodal Distribution

If the data has exactly two modes, we call it bimodal. If it has more than two, then it's *multimodal*. Multimodal information is often discarded, because it's not only hard to describe, it probably has little statistical value for us. Simply put, it doesn't tell you anything useful.

SAMPLE VERSUS POPULATION

In real business, statistics usually involves *samples*, not whole populations. You get a sample by, say, surveying 1,000 people about Smudge Fudge, instead of trying to find and interrogate all possible buyers of Smudge Fudge—an impossible task. Because samples are so important, the ability to judge the accuracy of samples is an important key to business statistics.

If you want to talk technical statistics-talk, you should know a few terms that statisticians use in precise ways. When dealing with sample data, use the term *sample statistics*. When dealing with whole populations, use the term *population parameters*. As we've said, most of the time you'll be doing the former.

The actual formulas used are also different for sample and population. Samples use *x*-bar for the mean and the Greek letter *mu* for the population mean.

Sample mean:

$$\overline{x} = \Sigma \frac{x_i}{n} = \frac{x_1 + x_2 + \ldots + x_n}{n}$$

Population mean:

$$\mu = \Sigma \frac{x_i}{N} = \frac{x_1 + x_2 + \ldots + x_n}{N}$$

Where n is the number in the sample, and N is the number in the population.

In more technical texts, the standard deviation for the population is represented by the letter s, while a sample is represented by the Greek letter σ.

BIAS—A CONTINUING PROBLEM IN STATISTICS

Bias as a statistical concept can mean two different things. Both have to do with faulty or slanted information. Bias can mean that the collected data itself is not a good representation of the facts. Methods of data collection can introduce bias into the data: For example, people might be more positive if a surveyor wears upscale clothes rather than casual ones.

Another definition of bias pertains to how well a sample represents the whole population. For instance, if a person conducting a survey in a shopping mall only approached people who looked easy to approach, the survey would probably be slanted, because the data collected would only reflect the opinions of friendly-looking people, not all the people in the mall. The survey sample is not representative of the whole population. If a survey sample is representative, then the sample itself is said to be an unbiased estimator of the population. We can then use the mathematical methods of statistics to interpret our data.

STATISTICS DON'T LIE

Let's be clear about it: Statistics are just dry, objective mathematics. The people who present information, however, may have a particular point of view, and consequently only give part of the story. If the information proves faulty, don't blame statistics. It's the people manipulating the data who present information in a misleading way. Trust statistics, but always be aware of the human factor in any statistical presentation.

SUMMARY

Statistics is the mathematical method by which researchers gather, analyze, represent and interpret numerical data. The mean, mode, and median are measures of the central tendencies of a distribution, and the range, variance, and standard deviation are measures of the variability of a distribution.

A *histogram* is a simple frequency diagram. It represents the frequency with which values occur in a sample.

A *stem-and-leaf* diagram gives a quick visual representation of statistical information, and is especially useful when you want to compare two sets of data.

The *bell-shaped curve* represents the frequency distribution of values in a sample. It accurately represents many real-world events in business, science, and our daily lives. It's called not only the bell-shaped curve or the bell curve, but also the normal curve, the normal distribution, the frequency distribution, and more technically, the Gaussian curve.

The *mean*, or average, is the value obtained by adding the values in a sample and dividing by the number of values. The *median* is the midpoint of the set of value—the number in the middle, like the median strip on the highway. The mode is the most common data value.

A *skewed* distribution is not symmetrical.

The *range* is how dispersed a distribution is, the difference between the maximum and minimum data values. An *outlier* is a very small or very large value, far removed from the other values in the sample. *Variance* is a measure of the dispersion of all the values in a sample. It is based on the difference between each value in the set and the mean. The *standard deviation* is the square root of the variance, and represents the most important description of dispersion.

A *z score* is the number of standard deviations. A z score of 2 means that a value is 2 standard deviations from the mean.

The *area under the curve* represents all the data values in a sample. The entire area under the curve represents 100% of the possibilities; collectively, these values have a probability of 1.

The percentage of events under the standard curve:

68.26%—one standard deviation
95.44%—two standard deviations
99.74%—three standard deviations
99.99976%—six sigma, or six standard deviations

Area Under the Curve

z	.00	.01	.02	.03	.04	.05	.06	.07	.08	.09
0.0	.0000	.0040	.0080	.0120	.0160	.0199	.0239	.00279	.0319	.0359
0.1	.0398	.0438	.0478	.0517	.0557	.0596	.0636	.0675	.0714	.0753
0.2	.0793	.083 2	.0871	.0910	.0948	.0987	.1026	.1064	.1103	.1141
0.3	.1179	.1217	.1255	.1293	.1331	.1368	.1406	.1443	.1480	.1517
0.4	.1554	.1591	.1628	.1664	.1700	.1736	.1772	.1808	.1844	.1879
0.5	.1915	.1950	.1985	.2019	.2054	.2088	.2123	.2157	.2190	.2224
0.6	.2257	.2291	.2324	.2357	.2389	.2422	.2454	.2486	.2518	.2549
0.7	.2580	.2612	.2642	.2673	.2704	.2734	.2764	.2794	.2823	.2852
0.8	.2881	.2910	.2939	.2967	.2995	.3023	.3051	.3078	.3106	.3133
0.9	.3159	.3186	.3212	.3238	.3264	.3289	.3315	.3340	.3365	.3389
1.0	.3413	.3438	.3461	.3485	.3508	.3531	.3554	.3577	.3599	.3621
1.1	.3643	.3665	.3686	.3708	.3729	.3749	.3770	.3790	.3810	.3830
1.2	.3849	.3869	.3888	.3908	.3925	.3944	.3962	.3980	.3997	.4015
1.3	.4032	.4049	.4066	.4082	.4099	.4115	.4131	.4147	.4162	.4177
1.4	.4192	.4207	.4222	.4236	.4251	.4265	.4279	.4292	.4306	.4319
1.5	.4332	.4345	.4357	.4370	.4382	.4394	.4406	.4418	.4429	.4441
1.6	.4452	.4463	.4474	.4484	.4495	.4505	.4515	.4525	.4535	.4545
1.7	.4554	.4564	.4573	.4582	.4591	.4599	.4608	.4616	.4625	.4633
1.8	.4641	.4649	.4656	.4664	.4671	.4678	.4686	.4693	.4699	.4706
1.9	.4713	.4719	.4726	.4732	.4738	.4744	.4750	.4756	.4761	.4767
2.0	.4772	.4778	.4783	.4788	.4793	.4798	.4803	.4808	.4812	.4817
2.1	.4821	.4826	.4830	.4834	.4838	.4842	.4846	.4850	.4854	.4857
2.2	.4861	.4864	.4868	.4871	.4875	.4878	.4881	.4884	.4887	.4890
2.3	.4893	.4896	.4898	.4901	.4904	.4906	.4909	.4911	.4913	.4916
2.4	.4918	.4920	.4922	.4925	.4927	.4929	.4931	.4932	.4934	.4936
2.5	.4938	.4940	.4941	.4943	.4945	.4946	.4948	4949	.4951	.4952
2.6	.4953	.4955	.4956	.4957	.4959	.4960	.4961	.4962	.4963	.4964
2.7	.4965	.4966	.4967	.4968	.4969	.4970	.4971	.4972	.4973	.4974
2.8	.4974	.4975	.4976	.4977	.4977	.4978	.4979	.4979	.4980	.4981
2.9	.4981	.4982	.4982	.4983	.4984	.4984	.4985	.4985	.4986	.4986
3.0	.4986	.4987	.4987	.4989	.4988	.4989	.4989	.4989	.4990	.4990

13

Statistics: Sampling and Probability

Because we don't, or can't, gather information from entire populations, we usually work instead with samples of the population, the next best thing. When we select samples and relate them to the population, we deal with probabilities. Consequently, probabilities and statistics are inexorably intertwined, and we get to play with such terms as *random, central limit theorem, 5% significance level,* and the *null hypothesis.*

The two most common concerns about any sample relate to its size and quality. These concerns can be formulated in question form:

- How large a sample do you need?

- How accurate do you want to be?

Beyond these questions, we assume that the selection of items or people for our sample is essentially random.

Random selections are just that—items selected in an non-ordered way, both non-organized and non-sequential. To be able to do this on a practical level, we try to select items, people, or what-have-you, in a manner that is both unbiased and independent—unbiased meaning that all units have the same chance of being selected, and independent meaning that selecting one item has no influence on the selection of other items.

Regression to the mean in statistics means that the sample will be similar to the whole population, when the sample size is large enough. As may seem obvious, the larger the sample gets, the more accurately it will represent the whole population, as long as the items selected are chosen at random. As a sample grows in size, probability dictates that it will become more similar in characteristics to the population as a whole.

The *central limit theorem* puts the same idea another way. If you take larger and larger samples, the theorem says, the distributions of the means of the samples will tend toward the mean of the normal distribution, even if the population isn't normal. As a result, you can still use calculations of the normal distribution even if you don't know the actual distribution of the population.

Suppose you survey several samples of the same population, and each time you get slightly different results. For each sample, the mean and standard deviation are just a little different. Does this mean you made a mistake? Probably not. There will always be slight differences between any two samples taken from a given population.

The *standard error* is a statistical calculation determining how imperfect a sample is. It's also called the standard error of estimate. It's equal to the standard deviation divided by the square root of the number of observations: $\dfrac{\sigma}{\sqrt{n}}$ where is the standard deviation and n is the number of items in the sample.

For example, if the standard deviation of an entire population is 25, and you take a series of samples of 100, you would expect the standard error to be 2.5: $\dfrac{25}{\sqrt{100}} = 2.5$

WHY 5%, OR .05 SIGNIFICANCE?

Significance is just what it sounds like: the degree of meaning in any statistical result. Significance is usually measured in terms of percentage difference from the norm. The two most common levels of significance employed by statisticians are 5% (.05) and 1% (.01). Although it's difficult to pinpoint the origin of the 5% significance level, one reference goes back to 1925, in R.A. Fisher's book, *Statistical Methods for Research Workers*. Fisher suggested that a 5% deviation from the norm would be a good point at which to decide that a statistical result has significance. He was of the opinion that all results should be rejected if they didn't meet this minimum test.

Since then, the 5% level of significance has slowly come to be accepted as a standard. Some researchers have questioned this test as being too large; they claim that results that differ less from the norm might still be meaningful. These researchers suggest a 1% level as a criterion for significance. Both of these levels make some sense, in that they relate mathematically to two and three standard deviations, respectively. Two deviations are approximately 95% accurate, and three standard deviations, 99%.

DEGREES OF FREEDOM

One of the more difficult features to grasp in statistics is what seems to be an almost minor term: *Degree of freedom*. It's used in a number of tests, so that we have to deal with it. In most cases it's equal to the number of observations minus 1. If you have taken 10 observations, then there are 9 degrees of freedom.

Perhaps the best way to understand this term is to think that if you are using 1 observation out of 10, then you have 9 options left, or 9 degrees of freedom.

THE NULL HYPOTHESIS, OR HOW TO THINK BACKWARDS

It's often difficult to prove positive hypotheses beyond all doubt. For example, suppose 16 people were interviewed, and 75% said they preferred Smudge Fudge over Sludge Fudge. The question is: What is the probability that this result was sheer chance? Enter the *null hypothesis*. It's a technique that has been developed to test just such a result.

The null hypothesis is a backward assumption. The assumption is deliberately made that the results obtained are by chance only. If this can be proved, then the results are no good for the researcher. If the null hypothesis is disproved, however, then the results of the sample can be used. Thus, we have avoided trying to prove the positive beyond all doubt.

At first this double-negative thinking is confusing, but it becomes understandable after working with specific problems.

The null hypothesis is written as H_0 and the non-chance hypothesis is written as H_1, or sometimes as H_a, for alternative hypothesis.

Here are the steps:

1. Formulate the null hypothesis.

2. Identify the statistic that will assess the null hypothesis.

3. Determine the probability that the null hypothesis is correct.

4. Compare that probability to a fixed level of significance, most commonly .05 or .01 level of significance.

What we are trying to do is avoid faulty thinking—specifically, what are called Type I and Type II errors:

> **Type I error:** This error occurs when a true hypothesis is rejected, for whatever reason.

> **Type II error:** This error occurs when a false hypothesis is accepted, for whatever reason.

THE "STUDENT'S t TEST"

The *student's t test* is a statistical test comparing the *means* of two distributions to see how alike they are. It is also called the *t test* or *t distribution*, or referred to as the *t table*. The *t* test is an examination of data to determine the level of confidence that may be placed in that data. William Grosset, a consultant to the Guinness Brewery in Dublin, wrote on this subject under the pseudonym "Student," and the name has stuck to this day.

When we described the central limit theorem, we said that if you take larger and larger samples, the distributions of the means of the samples will tend toward the mean of the normal distribution, even if the population isn't normal. The main difference between a sample curve and a normal curve is that the sample curve is usually flatter than the normal curve. The numbers are more dispersed on average. We use the degrees of freedom and the level of significance we wish to apply. We also assume for the *t test* that the distribution is a normal one.

For example, suppose you have to examine the number of days it takes to deliver catalogs to your customers. You take 15 random samples, and find that the mean (average) delivery time is 11.9 days. Your data looks like this:

Number of days	Number of days squared
15	225
14	196
10	100
12	144
12	144
11	121
14	196
8	64
10	100
11	121
15	144
15	225
9	81
10	100
15	225
178	2,186
Σx_i	Σx_i^2

$$\bar{x} = 11.9$$

We use the following formula for the standard deviation for the samples, and get 2.3:

$$\text{standard deviation of samples} = \sqrt{\frac{\Sigma x_i^2 - \frac{(\Sigma x_i)^2}{n}}{\text{degrees of freedom}}}$$

$$= \sqrt{\frac{2,186 - \frac{(178)^2}{15}}{14}}$$

$$= 2.3$$

Now we check the t table, looking up a confidence level of .05, which is a 95% level of confidence, and 14 degrees of freedom. Below is a part of the full table appearing at the end of the chapter. With 14 degrees of freedom and the .05 level of confidence, we get 1.761.

Degrees of freedom	Level of significance .05
13	1.771
14	1.761
15	1.761
15	1.753
16	1.746
17	1.740

Having now obtained this t value, we can enter it in our formula for the mean of our sample:

$$\text{days for delivery} = \text{mean} \pm \frac{t \times \text{sample deviation}}{\sqrt{n}}$$

$$= 11.9 \pm \frac{1.761 \times 2.3}{\sqrt{15}}$$

$$= 11.9 \pm 1.0$$

So, with a sample mean of +1 to -1, we can be 95% sure that the mean number of days it takes to deliver your catalogs is between 12.9 days and 10.9 days.

"F DISTRIBUTION" OR RATIO

A statistical test comparing the variances or standard deviations of two distributions to see how alike they are is called the F *distribution* or the F *ratio*. If the ratio of the sample variances is larger than the value of F given in the table, then there is too much difference between them for both samples to be valid.

Let's say that you have two samples of 10 and 15 values, respectively, and you want to know whether the results obtained from these samples are significant. Let's say that the variance of the scores of the first sample was 7.5 and the second 3.2. The ratio is then 7.5 divided by 3.2, which equals 2.34.

Let's say we want to compare our samples to the .05 significance level, to see whether they are significantly different. To find the degrees of freedom, we look at the sizes of the two samples. We subtract one from 10 and from 15, to get 9 and 14. The two samples thus have degrees of freedom of 9 and 14, respectively. We then consult our F table and obtain 3.02. The table shows a top figure for .05 level of significance (3.02) and a bottom figure for .01 level of significance (5.00):

Numerator of ratio

		11	12	14
Denominator of ratio	7	3.60 6.54	3.57 6.47	3.52 6.35
	8	3.31 5.74	3.28 5.67	3.23 5.56
	9	3.10 5.18	3.07 5.11	(3.02) 5.00
	10	2.94 4.78	3.07 4.71	2.86 4.60

Since at a 05 level of significance our F table shows 3.02, and our ratio is 2.34, which is well within our F table value, we can say that the two distributions are not significantly different.

BECOME FRIENDLY WITH THE "CHI SQUARE TEST"

The *chi square test* compares the frequencies of two distributions to see if they are alike or not. In statistics texts it is usually referred to as determining "the goodness-of-fit."

For small sample sizes, the *binomial probability distribution* is often used; this technique is covered next. When samples are large, or when there are many outcomes, not just two, then we turn to the *chi square test*.

It is written as x^2, from the Greek letter *chi*. The actual formula looks like this: $x^2 = \Sigma \dfrac{(f_0 - f_e)^2}{f_e}$

where f_o is the observed frequency in the sample and f_e is the expected frequency in the population as a whole.

This formula can be summarized this way: The sum of the squares of all the differences between the observed and expected results are divided by the expected results.

Let's look at an example. Say your company produces widgets, and there are ten inspectors that check for their accuracy. (We'll assume here that quality control is done this way, instead of the newer *total quality management* (TQM) method in which each individual worker is responsible for his own quality.) You carefully document each inspector's work:

Each Inspector	Number of rejects f_o	Expected frequency of rejects f_e	$(f_o - f_e)$	$(f_o - f_e)^2$	$\dfrac{(f_o - f_e)^2}{f_e}$
1	15	10	5	25	25
2	3	10	−7	49	4.9
3	7	10	−3	9	.9
4	8	10	−2	4	.4
5	5	10	−5	25	2.5
6	12	10	2	4	.4
7	11	10	1	1	.1
8	13	10	3	9	.9
9	9	10	−1	1	.1
10	17	10	7	49	4.9
	100	100			17.6

degrees of freedom = 9

To use the results, the degree of freedom of the sample is required. The degree of freedom is the number of independent comparisons made in computing the value of x^2. As explained earlier, you can think about degrees of freedom as the number of observations that are free to vary. We usually use the number of observations minus one (since you are calculating with one of the variables, leaving the remaining variables free to vary). For instance, if 10 inspectors were testing the quality of products, we would set the degrees of freedom at 9.

We also have to determine to what level of significance we want to judge this matter. That is, we want to know at what level of certainty to reject the null hypothesis. Let's use the standard .05.

We can now consult the table usually called the "values of x^2" of which a part is shown here; the full table is at the end of the chapter:

	0.050
1	3.84146
2	5.99147
3	7.81473
4	9.48773
5	11.0705
6	12.5916
7	14.0671
8	15.5073
9	(16.9190)
10	18.3070
11	19.6751
12	21.0261
13	22.3621
14	23.6848

Degrees of freedom

The table shows 16.92, meaning if our answer is greater than this, then it's significant. Our answer of 17.6 is indeed larger, showing this to be a significantly large answer. In other words, some inspectors are rejecting more widgets than others.

BINOMIAL PROBABILITIES

Binomial is a technical math term meaning "two numbers." Binomial sampling means sampling that separates the sample into two groups, perhaps dividing employed and unemployed, or buyers and nonbuyers. Separating people by more than two categories—say, weekly buyers, monthly buyers, yearly buyers, and so on—doesn't work. A sample must be split into only two groups to be considered binomial.

To use the table, we need to know the probability that a given item in the sample will be in one of your two subgroups. You must also know the sample size. For instance, if you are told that 2 out of 10 people watch a certain TV show, what would be the probability in a sample of 10 people of finding 2 people who watch it? A full table is at the end of the chapter, but a piece of it is below.

Level of significance

		0.050
9	1	0.630
	2	0.299
	3	0.063
	4	0.008
	5	0.001
	6	
Sample size	7	
	8	
	9	
10	0	0.599
	1	0.315
	2	0.075
	3	0.010
	4	0.001
	5	

The answer is circled, .075. That's 7.5%, less than 10%.

BAYES' THEOREM—OR, THE CASE OF FALSE POSITIVES

Another issue involving probability in statistics is the case of *false positives*. A false positive occurs when a test designed to detect a condition (like, for example, the presence of malaria virus in a patient) incorrectly gives a positive result. *Bayes' Theorem*, named after Thomas Bayes, a minister in England, 1744-1809, is a statistical method by which the number of false positives for a given test is estimated. It's important for procedures that are not 100% precise, like many medical tests. People who receive blood tests may test positive for a particular disease, only to find after further testing that they do not have the disease after all. This is understandably stressful for everyone, so the importance of knowing how many false positives to expect is obvious.

Let's say that there's a disease that affects one out of every 1,000 Americans. Assume that the test never fails to give a positive reading for someone who has the disease. Further, after additional study, let's say we've found that 2% of the tests give false positive readings, meaning that for every 100 people tested, two people who do not have the disease will get test results that say they do. Here's a look at the various probabilities at work in this situation:

Probability that a person has the disease: .001 (1 out of 1,000)
Probability of a positive test: .99
Probability of a false positive test: .02
Probability of having the disease if there is a positive test: .047
Thus, fewer than 5% of those who test positive will actually have the disease. The moral here is to double-check the results.

TWO OF YOU HAVE THE SAME BIRTHDAY?

Speaking of probability, here's a question for you. How large a group would it take to make it virtually certain that two people in the group shared a birthday?

We'll even make it multiple choice:

(A)   365

(B)   180

(C)   95

(D)   23

The answer is 23, believe it or not. Now, remember we did not say two people with a specific birthday, like April 1. We only asked for two people with the same birthday, whatever that date may be. It turns out that in a group of 23 people chosen at random, there is about a 95% chance that two people will have the same birthday. If you wanted to be 50% sure, you might want to round up to 25 or 30.

SUMMARY

Random selections are selections that are nonordered, nonorganized and nonsequential.

Regression to the mean means that a sample will be similar to the whole population when the sample size is large enough.

The *central limit theorem* says that as you take larger and larger samples, the distributions of the means of the samples will tend toward the mean of the normal distribution, even if the population isn't normal.

The *standard error* determines how imperfect the sample is. It's also called the standard error of estimate, and is equal to the standard deviation divided by the square root of the number of observations

The two most common *levels of significance* used are 5% (.05) or 1% (.01).

The *degree of freedom* is usually equal to one less than the number of values in the sample.

The *null hypothesis* is a backward assumption, specifically the statement that the results obtained in a study were obtained by pure chance and therefore have no meaning. If this can be proved, then the results are useless to the researcher. If the null hypothesis is disproved, however, then the results of the sample can be considered meaningful. In this way researchers avoid the difficult task of proving the positive beyond all doubt.

The *student's t test* compares the means of two distributions to see how much alike they are.

The *F distribution* or *F ratio* compares the variances or standard deviations of two distributions to see how much alike they are.

The *chi square test* compares the frequencies of two distributions to see if they are alike or not. This usually is referred to as the goodness-of-fit.

Binomial probabilities refers to a way of comparing results for two groups, such as buyers and nonbuyers.

Bayes' Theorem deals with the issue of false positives in statistics.

T TABLE

LEVELS OF CONFIDENCE		
Degrees of freedom	.05	.01
1	6.314	31.821
2	2.920	6.965
3	2.353	4.541
4	2.132	3.747
5	2.015	3.365
6	1.943	3.143
7	1.895	2.998
8	1.860	2.896
9	1.833	2.821
10	1.812	2.764
11	1.796	2.718
12	1.782	2.681
13	1.771	2.650
14	1.761	2.624
15	1.753	2.602
16	1.746	2.583
17	1.740	2.567
18	1.734	2.552
19	1.729	2.539
20	1.725	2.528
21	1.721	2.518
22	1.717	2.508
23	1.714	2.500
24	1.711	2.492
25	1.708	2.485

F TEST

Degrees of Freedom (Part One)

Numerator of Ratio

		1	2	3	4	5	6	7	8	9
	1	161	200	216	225	230	234	237	239	241
		4,052	**4,999**	**5,403**	**5,625**	**5,764**	**5,859**	**5,928**	**5,981**	**6,022**
	2	18.51	19.00	19.16	19.25	19.30	19.33	19.36	19.37	19.38
		98.49	**99.00**	**99.17**	**99.25**	**99.30**	**99.33**	**99.34**	**99.36**	**99.38**
	3	10.13	9.55	9.28	9.12	9.01	8.94	8.88	8.84	8.81
		34.12	**30.82**	**29.46**	**28.71**	**28.24**	**27.91**	**27.67**	**27.49**	**27.34**
	4	7.71	6.94	6.59	6.39	6.26	6.16	6.09	6.04	6.00
		21.20	**18.00**	**16.69**	**15.98**	**15.52**	**15.21**	**14.98**	**14.80**	**14.66**
	5	6.61	5.79	5.41	5.19	5.05	4.95	4.88	4.82	4.78
		16.26	**13.27**	**12.06**	**11.39**	**10.97**	**10.67**	**10.45**	**10.27**	**10.15**
	6	5.99	5.14	4.76	4.53	4.39	4.28	4.21	4.15	4.10
		13.74	**10.92**	**9.78**	**9.15**	**8.75**	**8.47**	**8.26**	**8.10**	**7.98**
	7	5.59	4.74	4.35	4.12	3.97	3.87	3.79	3.73	3.68
		12.25	**9.55**	**8.45**	**7.85**	**7.46**	**7.19**	**7.00**	**6.84**	**6.71**
	8	5.32	4.46	4.07	3.84	3.69	3.58	3.50	3.44	3.39
		11.26	**8.65**	**7.59**	**7.01**	**6.63**	**6.37**	**6.19**	**6.03**	**5.91**
	9	5.12	4.26	3.86	3.63	3.48	3.37	3.29	3.23	3.18
		10.56	**8.02**	**6.99**	**6.42**	**6.06**	**5.80**	**5.62**	**5.47**	**5.35**
Denominator of Ratio	10	4.96	4.10	3.71	3.48	3.33	3.22	3.14	3.07	3.02
		10.04	**7.56**	**6.55**	**5.99**	**5.64**	**5.39**	**5.21**	**5.06**	**4.95**
	11	4.84	3.98	3.59	3.36	3.20	3.09	3.01	2.95	2.90
		9.65	**7.20**	**6.22**	**5.67**	**5.32**	**5.07**	**4.88**	**4.74**	**4.63**
	12	4.75	3.88	3.49	3.26	3.11	3.00	2.92	2.85	2.80
		9.33	**6.93**	**5.95**	**5.41**	**5.06**	**4.82**	**4.65**	**4.50**	**4.39**
	14	4.60	3.74	3.34	3.11	2.96	2.85	2.77	2.70	2.65
		8.86	**6.51**	**5.56**	**5.03**	**4.69**	**4.46**	**4.28**	**4.14**	**4.03**
	16	4.49	3.63	3.24	3.01	2.85	2.74	2.66	2.59	2.54
		8.53	**6.23**	**5.29**	**4.77**	**4.44**	**4.20**	**4.03**	**3.89**	**3.78**
	18	4.41	3.55	3.16	2.93	2.77	2.66	2.58	2.51	2.46
		8.28	**6.01**	**5.09**	**4.58**	**4.25**	**4.01**	**3.85**	**3.71**	**3.60**
	20	4.35	3.49	3.10	2.87	2.71	2.60	2.52	2.45	2.40
		8.10	**5.85**	**4.94**	**4.43**	**4.10**	**3.87**	**3.71**	**3.56**	**3.45**
	25	4.24	3.38	2.99	2.76	2.60	2.49	2.41	2.34	2.28
		7.77	**5.57**	**4.68**	**4.18**	**3.86**	**3.63**	**3.46**	**3.32**	**3.21**
	30	4.17	3.32	2.92	2.69	2.53	2.42	2.34	2.27	2.21
		7.56	**5.39**	**4.51**	**4.02**	**3.70**	**3.47**	**3.30**	**3.17**	**3.06**
	40	4.08	3.23	2.84	2.61	2.45	2.34	2.25	2.18	2.12
		7.31	**5.18**	**4.31**	**3.83**	**3.51**	**3.29**	**3.12**	**2.99**	**2.88**
	50	4.03	3.18	2.79	2.56	2.40	2.29	2.20	2.13	2.07
		7.17	**5.06**	**4.20**	**3.72**	**3.41**	**3.18**	**3.02**	**2.88**	**2.78**

egrees of Freedom (Part Two)

Numerator of Ratio

	10	11	12	14	16	20	24	30	40	50
1	242	243	244	245	246	248	249	250	251	252
	6,056	**6,082**	**6,106**	**6,142**	**6,169**	**6,208**	**6,234**	**6,258**	**6,286**	**6,302**
2	19.39	19.40	19.41	19.42	19.43	19.44	19.45	19.46	19.47	19.47
	99.40	**99.41**	**99.42**	**99.43**	**99.44**	**99.45**	**99.46**	**99.47**	**99.48**	**99.48**
3	8.78	8.76	8.74	8.71	8.69	8.66	8.64	8.62	8.60	8.58
	27.23	**27.13**	**27.05**	**26.92**	**26.83**	**26.69**	**26.60**	**26.50**	**26.41**	**26.35**
4	5.96	5.93	5.91	5.87	5.84	5.80	5.77	5.74	5.71	5.70
	14.54	**14.45**	**14.37**	**14.24**	**14.15**	**14.02**	**13.93**	**13.83**	**13.74**	**13.69**
5	4.74	4.70	4.68	4.64	4.60	4.56	4.53	4.50	4.46	4.44
	10.05	**9.96**	**9.89**	**9.77**	**9.68**	**9.55**	**9.47**	**9.38**	**9.29**	**9.24**
6	4.06	4.03	4.00	3.96	3.92	3.87	3.84	3.81	3.77	3.75
	7.87	**7.79**	**7.72**	**7.60**	**7.52**	**7.39**	**7.31**	**7.23**	**7.14**	**7.09**
7	3.63	3.60	3.57	3.52	3.49	3.44	3.41	3.38	3.34	3.32
	6.62	**6.54**	**6.47**	**6.35**	**6.27**	**6.15**	**6.07**	**5.98**	**5.90**	**5.85**
8	3.34	3.31	3.28	3.23	3.20	3.15	3.12	3.08	3.05	3.03
	5.82	**5.74**	**5.67**	**5.56**	**5.48**	**5.36**	**5.28**	**5.20**	**5.11**	**5.06**
9	3.13	3.10	3.07	3.02	2.98	2.93	2.90	2.86	2.82	2.80
	5.26	**5.18**	**5.11**	**5.00**	**4.92**	**4.80**	**4.73**	**4.64**	**4.56**	**4.51**
10	2.97	2.94	2.91	2.86	2.82	2.77	2.74	2.70	2.67	2.64
	4.85	**4.78**	**4.71**	**4.60**	**4.52**	**4.41**	**4.33**	**4.25**	**4.17**	**4.12**
11	2.86	2.82	2.79	2.74	2.70	2.65	2.61	2.57	2.53	2.50
	4.54	**4.46**	**4.40**	**4.29**	**4.21**	**4.10**	**4.02**	**3.94**	**3.86**	**3.80**
12	2.76	2.72	2.69	2.64	2.60	2.54	2.50	2.46	2.42	2.40
	4.30	**4.22**	**4.16**	**4.05**	**3.98**	**3.86**	**3.78**	**3.70**	**3.61**	**3.56**
14	2.60	2.56	2.53	2.48	2.44	2.39	2.35	2.31	2.27	2.24
	3.94	**3.86**	**3.80**	**3.70**	**3.62**	**3.51**	**3.43**	**3.34**	**3.26**	**3.21**
16	2.49	2.45	2.42	2.37	2.33	2.28	2.24	2.20	2.16	2.13
	3.69	**3.61**	**3.55**	**3.45**	**3.37**	**3.25**	**3.18**	**3.10**	**3.01**	**2.96**
18	2.41	2.37	2.34	2.29	2.25	2.19	2.15	2.11	2.07	2.04
	3.51	**3.44**	**3.37**	**3.27**	**3.19**	**3.07**	**3.00**	**2.91**	**2.83**	**2.78**
20	2.35	2.31	2.28	2.23	2.18	2.12	2.08	2.04	1.99	1.96
	3.37	**3.30**	**3.23**	**3.13**	**3.05**	**2.94**	**2.86**	**2.77**	**2.69**	**2.63**
25	2.24	2.20	2.16	2.11	2.06	2.00	1.96	1.92	1.87	1.84
	3.13	**3.05**	**2.99**	**2.89**	**2.81**	**2.70**	**2.62**	**2.54**	**2.45**	**2.40**
30	2.16	2.12	2.09	2.04	1.99	1.93	1.89	1.84	1.79	1.76
	2.98	**2.90**	**2.84**	**2.74**	**2.66**	**2.55**	**2.47**	**2.38**	**2.29**	**2.24**
40	2.07	2.04	2.00	1.95	1.90	1.84	1.79	1.74	1.69	1.66
	2.80	**2.73**	**2.66**	**2.56**	**2.49**	**2.37**	**2.29**	**2.20**	**2.11**	**2.05**
50	2.02	1.98	1.95	1.90	1.85	1.78	1.74	1.69	1.63	1.60
	2.70	**2.62**	**2.56**	**2.46**	**2.39**	**2.26**	**2.18**	**2.10**	**2.00**	**1.94**

Denominator of Ratio

CHI-SQUARE TEST

Levels of Significance

Degrees of Freedom	0.050	0.025	0.010	0.005
1	3.84146	5.02389	6.63490	7.87944
2	5.99147	7.37776	9.21034	10.5966
3	7.81473	9.34840	11.3449	12.8381
4	9.48773	11.1433	13.2767	14.8602
5	11.0705	12.8325	15.0863	16.7496
6	12.5916	14.4494	16.8119	18.5476
7	14.0671	16.0128	18.4753	20.2777
8	15.5073	17.5346	20.0902	21.9550
9	16.9190	19.0228	21.6660	23.5893
10	18.3070	20.4831	23.23093	25.1882
11	19.6751	21.9200	24.7250	26.7569
12	21.0261	23.3367	26.2170	28.2995
13	22.3621	24.7356	27.6883	29.8194
14	23.6848	26.1190	29.1413	31.3193
15	24.9958	27.4884	30.5779	32.8013
16	26.2962	28.8454	31.9999	34.2672
17	27.5871	30.1910	33.4087	35.7185
18	28.8693	31.5264	34.8053	37.1564
19	30.1435	32.8523	36.1908	38.5822
20	31.4104	34.1696	37.5662	39.9968
21	32.6705	35.4789	38.9321	41.4010
22	33.9244	36.7807	40.2894	42.7956
23	35.1725	38.0757	41.6384	44.1813
24	36.4151	39.3641	42.9798	45.5585
25	37.6525	40.6465	44.3141	46.9278
26	38.8852	41.9232	45.6417	48.2899
27	40.1133	43.1944	46.9630	49.6449
28	41.3372	44.4607	48.2782	50.9933
29	42.5569	45.7222	49.5879	52.3356
30	43.7729	46.9792	50.8922	53.6720
40	55.7585	59.3417	63.6907	66.7659
50	67.5048	71.4202	76.1539	79.4900
60	79.0819	83.2976	88.3794	91.9517
70	90.5312	95.0231	100.425	104.215
80	101.879	106.629	112.329	116.321
90	113.145	118.136	124.116	128.299
100	124.342	129.561	135.807	140.169

Probability

n	x	0.05	0.1	0.2	0.25	0.3	0.4	0.5	0.6	0.7	0.75	0.8	0.9	0.95
2	0	0.902	0.810	0.640	0.563	0.490	0.360	0.250	0.160	0.090	0.063	0.040	0.010	0.002
	1	0.095	0.180	0.320	0.375	0.420	0.480	0.500	0.480	0.420	0.375	0.320	0.180	0.095
	2	0.002	0.010	0.040	0.063	0.090	0.160	0.250	0.360	0.490	0.563	0.640	0.810	0.902
3	0	0.857	0.729	0.512	0.422	0.343	0.216	0.125	0.064	0.027	0.016	0.008	0.001	
	1	0.135	0.243	0.384	0.422	0.441	0.432	0.375	0.288	0.189	0.141	0.096	0.027	0.007
	2	0.007	0.027	0.096	0.141	0.189	0.288	0.375	0.432	0.441	0.422	0.384	0.243	0.135
	3		0.001	0.008	0.016	0.027	0.064	0.125	0.216	0.343	0.422	0.512	0.729	0.857
4	0	0.815	0.656	0.410	0.316	0.240	0.130	0.062	0.026	0.008	0.004	0.002		
	1	0.171	0.292	0.410	0.422	0.412	0.346	0.250	0.154	0.076	0.047	0.026	0.004	
	2	0.014	0.049	0.154	0.211	0.265	0.346	0.375	0.346	0.265	0.211	0.154	0.049	0.014
	3		0.004	0.026	0.047	0.076	0.154	0.250	0.346	0.412	0.422	0.410	0.292	0.171
	4			0.002	0.004	0.008	0.026	0.062	0.130	0.240	0.316	0.410	0.656	0.815
5	0	0.774	0.590	0.328	0.237	0.168	0.078	0.031	0.010	0.002	0.001			
	1	0.204	0.328	0.410	0.396	0.360	0.259	0.156	0.007	0.028	0.015	0.006		
	2	0.021	0.073	0.205	0.264	0.309	0.346	0.312	0.230	0.132	0.088	0.051	0.008	0.001
	3	0.001	0.008	0.051	0.088	0.132	0.230	0.312	0.346	0.309	0.274	0.205	0.073	0.021
	4			0.006	0.015	0.028	0.077	0.156	0.259	0.360	0.396	0.410	0.328	0.204
	5				0.001	0.002	0.010	0.031	0.078	0.168	0.237	0.328	0.590	0.774
6	0	0.735	0.531	0.262	0.178	0.118	0.047	0.016	0.004	0.001				
	1	0.232	0.354	0.393	0.356	0.303	0.187	0.094	0.037	0.010	0.004	0.002		
	2	0.031	0.098	0.246	0.297	0.324	0.311	0.234	0.138	0.060	0.033	0.015	0.001	
	3	0.002	0.015	0.082	0.132	0.185	0.276	0.132	0.276	0.185	0.132	0.082	0.015	0.002
	4		0.001	0.015	0.033	0.060	0.138	0.234	0.311	0.324	0.297	0.246	0.098	0.031
	5			0.002	0.004	0.010	0.037	0.094	0.187	0.303	0.356	0.393	0.354	0.232
	6					0.001	0.004	0.016	0.047	0.118	0.178	0.262	0.531	0.735
7	0	0.698	0.478	0.210	0.134	0.082	0.028	0.008	0.002					
	1	0.257	0.372	0.367	0.312	0.247	0.131	0.055	0.017	0.004	0.001			
	2	0.041	0.124	0.275	0.312	0.318	0.261	0.164	0.077	0.025	0.012	0.004		
	3	0.004	0.023	0.115	0.173	0.227	0.290	0.273	0.194	0.097	0.058	0.029	0.003	
	4		0.003	0.029	0.058	0.097	0.194	0.273	0.290	0.227	0.173	0.115	0.023	0.004
	5			0.004	0.012	0.025	0.077	0.164	0.261	0.318	0.312	0.275	0.124	0.041
	6				0.001	0.004	0.017	0.055	0.131	0.247	0.312	0.367	0.372	0.257
	7					0.002	0.008	0.028	0.082	0.134	0.210	0.478	0.698	
8	0	0.663	0.430	0.168	0.100	0.058	0.017	0.004	0.001					
	1	0.279	0.383	0.336	0.267	0.198	0.090	0.031	0.008	0.001				
	2	0.051	0.149	0.294	0.312	0.296	0.209	0.109	0.041	0.010	0.004	0.001		
	3	0.005	0.033	0.147	0.208	0.254	0.279	0.219	0.124	0.047	0.023	0.009		
	4		0.005	0.046	0.087	0.136	0.232	0.273	0.232	0.136	0.087	0.046	0.005	
	5			0.009	0.023	0.047	0.124	0.219	0.279	0.254	0.208	0.147	0.033	0.005
	6			0.001	0.004	0.010	0.041	0.109	0.209	0.296	0.312	0.294	0.149	0.051
	7					0.001	0.008	0.031	0.090	0.198	0.267	0.336	0.383	0.279
	8						0.001	0.004	0.017	0.058	0.100	0.168	0.430	0.663

BINOMIAL PROBABILITY DISTRIBUTION (CON'T.)

Probability

Sample Size	x	0.05	0.1	0.2	0.25	0.3	0.4	0.5	0.6	0.7	0.75	0.8	0.9	0.95
9	0	0.630	0.387	0.134	0.075	0.040	0.010	0.002						
	1	0.299	0.387	0.302	0.225	0.156	0.060	0.018	0.004					
	2	0.063	0.172	0.302	0.300	0.267	0.161	0.070	0.021	0.004	0.001			
	3	0.008	0.045	0.176	0.234	0.267	0.251	0.164	0.074	0.021	0.009	0.003		
	4	0.001	0.007	0.066	0.117	0.172	0.251	0.246	0.167	0.074	0.039	0.017	0.001	
	5		0.001	0.017	0.039	0.074	0.167	0.246	0.251	0.172	0.117	0.066	0.007	0.001
	6			0.003	0.009	0.021	0.074	0.164	0.251	0.267	0.234	0.176	0.045	0.008
	7				0.001	0.004	0.021	0.070	0.161	0.267	0.300	0.302	0.172	0.063
	8						0.004	0.018	0.060	0.156	0.225	0.302	0.387	0.299
	9							0.002	0.010	0.040	0.075	0.134	0.387	0.630
10	0	0.599	0.349	0.107	0.056	0.028	0.006	0.001						
	1	0.315	0.387	0.268	0.188	0.121	0.040	0.010	0.002					
	2	0.075	0.194	0.302	0.282	0.233	0.121	0.044	0.011	0.001				
	3	0.010	0.057	0.201	0.250	0.267	0.215	0.117	0.042	0.009	0.003	0.001		
	4	0.001	0.011	0.088	0.146	0.200	0.251	0.205	0.111	0.037	0.016	0.006		
	5		0.001	0.026	0.058	0.103	0.201	0.246	0.201	0.103	0.058	0.026	0.001	
	6			0.006	0.016	0.037	0.111	0.205	0.251	0.200	0.146	0.088	0.011	0.001
	7			0.001	0.003	0.009	0.042	0.117	0.215	0.267	0.250	0.201	0.057	0.010
	8					0.001	0.011	0.044	0.121	0.233	0.282	0.302	0.194	0.075
	9						0.002	0.010	0.040	0.121	0.188	0.268	0.387	0.315
	10							0.001	0.006	0.028	0.056	0.107	0.349	0.599
11	0	0.569	0.314	0.086	0.042	0.020	0.004							
	1	0.329	0.384	0.236	0.155	0.093	0.027	0.005	0.001					
	2	0.087	0.213	0.295	0.258	0.200	0.089	0.027	0.005	0.001				
	3	0.014	0.071	0.221	0.258	0.257	0.177	0.081	0.023	0.004	0.001			
	4	0.001	0.016	0.111	0.172	0.220	0.236	0.161	0.070	0.017	0.006	0.002		
	5		0.002	0.039	0.080	0.132	0.221	0.226	0.147	0.057	0.027	0.010		
	6			0.010	0.027	0.057	0.147	0.226	0.221	0.132	0.080	0.039	0.002	
	7			0.002	0.006	0.017	0.070	0.161	0.236	0.220	0.172	0.111	0.016	0.001
	8				0.001	0.004	0.023	0.081	0.177	0.257	0.258	0.221	0.071	0.014
	9					0.001	0.005	0.027	0.089	0.200	0.258	0.295	0.213	0.087
	10						0.001	0.005	0.027	0.093	0.155	0.236	0.384	0.329
	11								0.004	0.020	0.042	0.086	0.314	0.569
12	0	0.540	0.282	0.069	0.032	0.014	0.002							
	1	0.341	0.377	0.206	0.127	0.071	0.017	0.003						
	2	0.099	0.230	0.283	0.232	0.168	0.064	0.016	0.002					
	3	0.017	0.085	0.236	0.258	0.240	0.142	0.054	0.012	0.001				
	4	0.002	0.021	0.133	0.194	0.231	0.213	0.121	0.042	0.008	0.002	0.001		
	5		0.004	0.053	0.103	0.158	0.227	0.193	0.101	0.029	0.012	0.003		
	6			0.016	0.040	0.079	0.177	0.226	0.177	0.079	0.040	0.016		
	7			0.003	0.012	0.029	0.101	0.193	0.227	0.158	0.103	0.053	0.004	
	8			0.001	0.002	0.008	0.042	0.121	0.213	0.231	0.194	0.133	0.021	0.002
	9					0.001	0.012	0.054	0.142	0.240	0.258	0.236	0.085	0.017
	10						0.002	0.016	0.064	0.168	0.232	0.283	0.230	0.099
	11							0.003	0.017	0.071	0.127	0.206	0.377	0.341
	12								0.002	0.014	0.032	0.069	0.282	0.540

Probability

n	x	0.005	0.1	0.2	0.25	0.3	0.4	0.5	0.6	0.7	0.75	0.8	0.9	0.95
13	0	0.513	0.254	0.055	0.024	0.010	0.001							
	1	0.351	0.367	0.179	0.103	0.054	0.011	0.002						
	2	0.111	0.245	0.268	0.206	0.139	0.045	0.010	0.001					
	3	0.021	0.100	0.246	0.252	0.218	0.111	0.035	0.006	0.001				
	4	0.003	0.028	0.154	0.210	0.234	0.184	0.087	0.024	0.003				
	5		0.006	0.069	0.126	0.180	0.221	0.157	0.066	0.014	0.005	0.001		
	6		0.001	0.023	0.056	0.103	0.197	0.209	0.131	0.044	0.019	0.006		
	7			0.006	0.019	0.044	0.131	0.209	0.197	0.103	0.056	0.023	0.001	
	8			0.001	0.005	0.014	0.066	0.157	0.221	0.180	0.126	0.069	0.006	
	9				0.001	0.003	0.024	0.087	0.184	0.234	0.210	0.154	0.028	0.003
	10					0.001	0.006	0.035	0.111	0.218	0.252	0.246	0.100	0.021
	11						0.001	0.010	0.045	0.139	0.206	0.268	0.245	0.111
	12							0.002	0.011	0.054	0.103	0.179	0.367	0.351
	13								0.001	0.010	0.024	0.055	0.254	0.513
14	0	0.488	0.229	0.044	0.018	0.007	0.001							
	1	0.359	0.356	0.154	0.083	0.041	0.007	0.001						
	2	0.123	0.257	0.250	0.180	0.113	0.032	0.006	0.001					
	3	0.026	0.114	0.250	0.240	0.194	0.085	0.022	0.003					
	4	0.004	0.035	0.172	0.220	0.229	0.155	0.061	0.014	0.001				
	5		0.008	0.086	0.147	0.196	0.207	0.122	0.041	0.007	0.002			
	6		0.001	0.032	0.073	0.126	0.207	0.183	0.092	0.023	0.008	0.002		
	7			0.009	0.028	0.062	0.157	0.209	0.157	0.062	0.028	0.009		
	8			0.002	0.008	0.023	0.092	0.183	0.207	0.126	0.073	0.032	0.001	
	9				0.002	0.007	0.041	0.122	0.207	0.196	0.147	0.086	0.008	
	10					0.001	0.014	0.061	0.155	0.229	0.220	0.172	0.035	0.004
	11						0.003	0.022	0.805	0.194	0.240	0.250	0.114	0.026
	12						0.001	0.006	0.032	0.113	0.180	0.250	0.257	0.123
	13							0.001	0.007	0.041	0.083	0.154	0.356	0.359
	14								0.001	0.007	0.018	0.044	0.229	0.488
15	0	0.463	0.206	0.035	0.013	0.005								
	1	0.366	0.343	0.132	0.067	0.031	0.005							
	2	0.135	0.267	0.231	0.156	0.092	0.002	0.003						
	3	0.031	0.129	0.250	0.225	0.170	0.063	0.014	0.002					
	4	0.005	0.043	0.188	0.225	0.219	0.127	0.042	0.007	0.001				
	5	0.001	0.010	0.103	0.165	0.206	0.186	0.092	0.024	0.003	0.001			
	6		0.002	0.043	0.092	0.147	0.207	0.153	0.061	0.012	0.003	0.001		
	7			0.014	0.039	0.081	0.177	0.196	0.118	0.035	0.013	0.003		
	8			0.003	0.013	0.035	0.118	0.196	0.177	0.081	0.039	0.014		
	9				0.001	0.003	0.012	0.061	0.153	0.207	0.147	0.092	0.043	0.002
	10				0.001	0.003	0.024	0.092	0.186	0.206	0.165	0.103	0.010	0.001
	11					0.001	0.007	0.042	0.127	0.219	0.225	0.188	0.043	0.005
	12						0.002	0.014	0.063	0.170	0.225	0.250	0.129	0.031
	13							0.003	0.022	0.092	0.156	0.231	0.267	0.135
	14								0.005	0.031	0.067	0.132	0.343	0.366
	15									0.005	0.013	0.035	0.206	0.463

PART III

14

Statistics: Correlation

Correlation is the part of statistics that deals with the way in which two or more variables act together, or don't. It shows whether two or more variables are related, and how close that relationship is. Economics in particular grapples often with such questions: Does consumption correlate to income? Does employment correlate to wages? Does inflation correlate to the stock market? And so forth.

We generally look for three things when we analyze variables:

- Does a change in one variable usually trigger a change in another?

- If there is such a relationship, what is the magnitude of the change?

- Once a relationship is established, just how precisely can that relationship be described?

SCATTER DIAGRAMS AND CORRELATION COEFFICIENTS

To describe a statistical relationship, we can either show a graph, called a *scatter diagram,* or summarize the relationship using a correlation coefficient. The name scatter diagram, or *scattergram,* describes with fair accuracy how a relationship between two variables looks on a graph. The graph can show a trend or relationship, or only a seemingly random scattering of points:

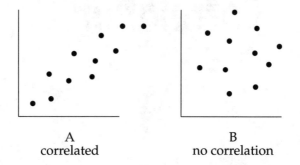

A
correlated

B
no correlation

Diagram A shows an upward trend or relationship, whereas diagram B shows an apparently random relationship. Just by observation, we would say that a correlation exists in diagram A but not in B.

The *regression line* is the straight line that best represents all the data points in a scatter diagram and is only meaningful when the data in the diagram show a relationship. A line for a random scattering of points is meaningless. We could, of course, just guess at the correct line and draw it in freehand, but there's a mathematical method to calculate it precisely:

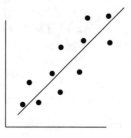

regression line

The *least squares method* is the mathematical method for determining the slope and position of this perfectly straight line. Its name comes from the fact that the regression line minimizes the total distance between it and each point on the graph. Mathematically, the straight line follows the general form for a linear equation:

$$y = ax + b$$

We can solve for a using one of the following equations:

$$a = \frac{\Sigma(x^i - \bar{x})(y^i - \bar{y})}{\Sigma(x^i - \bar{x})^2}$$

Or, to make your calculations easier:

$$a = \frac{\Sigma x^i y^i - (\Sigma x^i \Sigma)/n}{\Sigma x^{i2} - (\Sigma x^i)^2/n}$$

Once we know the value of a, we can solve for b:
Where:

$$b = \bar{y} - a\bar{x}$$

x^i is each value of x (one y the variables)
y^i is each value of the y (the other variable)
$\bar{x}$ is the mean for all x values
$\bar{y}$ is the mean for all y values
n is the number of observations

EXAMPLE: INTERNET CAFES

Let's say your small company has started several cafes with Internet-connected computers on each table. You sell cappuccino and latte in a congenial atmosphere. You started in smaller towns and have moved into larger towns over the past year. You now have 6 cafes, and want to be able to project your sales as you continue to open cafes in larger towns.

Here are the current sales figures for your stores and the populations of the towns they're situated in:

Internet Cafes

Cafe	Population (in 10,000s)	Sales (in $1,000s)
1	3	75
2	7	81
3	8	110
4	14	142
5	21	149
6	24	220

The first thing to do is plot the data values on a scatter diagram to see if we can discern a pattern or trend. We are asking the question: "Does a relationship exists between these two variables?" We'll let the x-axis represent the populations of the towns in increments of 10,000, and the y-axis represent the stores' sales in increments of $1,000:

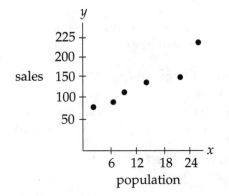

There seems to be a relationship—one with an upward trend to the right (meaning that sales and population tend to increase together). We can now calculate the least squares line using our data, solving for a and b in our linear equation:

	X_i	Y_i	X_iY_i	X_i^2	Y_i^2
1	3	75	225	9	5,625
2	7	81	567	49	6,561
3	8	110	880	64	12,100
4	14	142	1,988	196	20,164
5	21	149	3,129	441	22,201
6	24	220	5,280	576	48,400
	77	777	12,069	1,335	115,051
	Σx_i	Σy_i	Σx_iy_i	Σx_i^2	Σy_i^2

$$a = \frac{12,069 - (77)(777)/6}{1,335 - (77)^2/6}$$

$$a = \frac{2,097.5}{346.8}$$

$$a = 6.05 = 6 \text{ (rounded)}$$

Using this value for a, we can now solve for b:

$$b = \frac{777}{6} - 6\left(\frac{77}{6}\right)$$

$$b = 129.5 - 77$$

$$b = 52.5$$

Having obtained our values for a and b, we can now write the liner equation representing our two variables:

$$y = 6x + 52.5$$

Using this equation, we can then project an estimate of sales for an even larger town. We do this by extending the line to whatever population level we wish. For instance, if the town had a population of 50,000, our sales would be estimated, using the linear equation we just developed, at $352,500:

$$y = 6(50) + 52.5$$

$$y = 352.5 = \$352,000$$

Note that this equation does not reproduce the actual original observations, but is the best approximation of a straight line.

THE COEFFICIENT OF DETERMINATION, OR "HOW GOOD IS THE FIT?"

The next question we can ask is a more technical one: "How well does our line of regression fit our data?" We can answer the question using what is called the coefficient of determination or another related quantity, r^2. Using an equation similar to the one we used above, r^2 is the fraction of:

the numerator (top number):

$$numerator = \frac{\left[\Sigma x^i y^i - \left(\Sigma x^i \Sigma y^i\right)/n\right]^2}{\Sigma x_i^2 - \left(\Sigma x^i\right)^2 / n}$$

the denominator (bottom number):

$$denominator = \Sigma y_i^2 - \frac{\left(\Sigma y^i\right)^2}{n}$$

Solving for this fraction, we get the value .88, which is r^2:

$$numerator = \frac{\left[12,069 - (77)\,(777)/6\right]^2}{1,335 - (77)^2/6}$$

$$numerator = \frac{4,399,509}{346.8} = 12,686$$

$$denominator = 115,051 - \frac{(777)^2}{6}$$

$$denominator = 14,429$$

$$r^2 = \frac{12,686}{14,429} = .88$$

This calculation of r^2 gives us a numerical value indicating how well our relationship is correlated.

THE COEFFICIENT OF CORRELATION, POSITIVE OR NEGATIVE

The value of r^2 is always positive. By taking the square root of r^2, however, we get the *coefficient of correlation*, which can be either positive or negative.

The coefficient of correlation will be between +1 and -1. If the coefficient is exactly equal to +1, then the relationship is perfectly correlated. If it equals 0, then there is no correlation; and if it's exactly equal to -1, then it's perfectly correlated in the opposite direction. A scatter diagram of these three extremes looks like this:

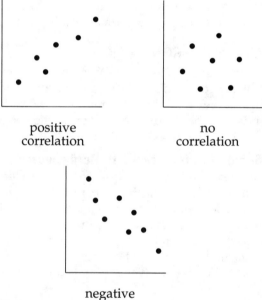

positive correlation

no correlation

negative correlation

In our example of Internet cafes, r^2 has a value of .88, which is quite close to 1, because the slope of our graph is positive, $r=+.93$.

BETA—A FRIEND TO INVESTORS

As an investor, you may have come across the term *beta*, also called *beta coefficient*. It is found through a calculation similar to the one shown above. The monthly performance of a particular stock or mutual fund is calculated along side the S&P 500 index. A 36-month period is usually selected. Those returns are then adjusted for risk-free returns by subtracting the T-bill rate (that's the rate of interest on treasury bills, which are considered a perfectly secure investment). A scatter diagram is plotted of the movements of a particular stock or mutual fund against the movements of S&P 500 index. The least squares line is then calculated for this graph. Solving for the slope of the line gives us the beta coefficient.

MULTIPLE CORRELATION AND REGRESSION ANALYSIS

There are business situations where we would like to test the correlation of many variables. For instance, in our Internet cafe problem, we might like to consider not only our population and sales variables, but also the average salary in the towns, the SAT scores at the local high school, or any other variable that we can believe might be correlated. By testing and correlating these variables, we might be able to refine the selection for our upcoming cafes.

NONLINEAR CORRELATION

We've used a straight line to represent our observations in this chapter. Not all correlations between variables have such a linear relationship, however. Some are geometrical, producing curves of various kinds. The basic form, however, is the straight line—and we therefore start with this assumption.

Caveat—Some Things Deserve to Be Repeated

When researchers find a correlation between variables, they can expect that approximately one time in twenty the correlation will be false! That is, it will show correlation, even to the .05 level of significance, but only by happenstance—pure luck at that particular time with those particular numbers. When you repeat your test at a later time, those variables will not show correlation, because the relationship was false to begin with. The moral: Handle correlations with care.

SUMMARY

A *scatter diagram* is a graph showing the relationship between two variables. A diagram of this kind can show a trend or relationship, or indicate the absence of a correlation by showing a random distribution.

A *regression line* is the straight line that best represents all the data points in the scatter diagram.

The *least squares method* is the mathematical method that determines the position and slope of the regression line.

The *coefficients of determination and correlation*, r^2 and r, express the closeness of the relationship between two variables. The value of r will be between +1 and -1. If r is exactly +1, then the relationship is perfectly correlated. If r equals 0, then there is no correlation; and if r equals −1, then your variables are perfectly correlated in the opposite direction.

Multiple regression analysis is the study of the relationship between three or more variables.

A caveat to be remembered: approximately one time in twenty, a correlation found by this mathematics will be false!

15

Spreadsheets

Spreadsheets, also called *worksheets*, are computer programs that allow numerical information to be input and manipulated. Spreadsheets are organized into grids of rectangular units known as *cells*. Each cell has an address, or location, that other cells can refer to. It's the ability of these cells to relate to each other that makes spreadsheets so powerful. It allows an entire spreadsheet, possibly containing hundreds of numbers, to readjust itself in response to a change in one quantity.

Cells are organized into *rows* and *columns*. Rows, which are horizontal, are usually referenced by numbers, while columns, which are vertical, are usually referenced by letters. For instance, cell D3 is in column D (the fourth column from the left) and row 3 (the 3rd row from the top). A formula in cell D3 can refer to and manipulate data from cell D5, for instance. The business applications of spreadsheets are numerous, often found in accounting, finance, sales, and marketing. The two most popular spreadsheet applications today are Microsoft Excel and Lotus 1-2-3.

Here's a simple example of a spreadsheet of financial information:

	A	B	C	D	E
1					
2					
3		Net present value:		$7,321	
4					
5		Discount rate:		12.00%	
6					
7		Year 1:		(10,000)	
8		Year 2:		(6,000)	
9		Year 3:		500	
10		Year 4:		12,000	
11		Year 5:		23,000	
12					
13					
14					
15					

You can see that besides numbers, words can be entered as titles, like "Net present value," "Discount rate," "Year 1," and so forth. Numbers are entered in cell D5 representing the interest rate, and cells D7 through D11 representing cash flows. Cells can be programmed to automatically assign dollar signs, percentages and other formats to numbers. These formats are not usually entered directly with the numbers, but through a sequence of formatting instructions. Some of the newer versions of the big spreadsheet programs guess intelligently at the appropriate formatting. In cell D5, just the raw number .12 is entered, but then formatted to appear as a percentage to two decimal places, or three, or whatever you want. In cell D7, the raw number —10000— is entered without commas, but is then formatted for thousands so that it appears with a comma (10,000). You can also specify either parentheses or the minus sign to show a negative number.

In this example, the number shown in cell D3, $7,321, was not entered by hand. Instead, the standard worksheet function for net present value was entered in the cell, causing the cell to calculate this value based on data in other cells. The two major spreadsheet programs denote formulas and functions with different initial symbols: Lotus 1-2-3 uses @, the "at" sign, while Excel uses =, the equal sign. The @ sign is used in this chapter in deference to the author, who has used Lotus for about 15 years. Also, although there are only slight differences between the expressions of functions in Excel and Lotus, the Lotus nomenclature is used in this book.

The worksheet function for net present value is: @NPV(int,range). When the actual cell references are included, the actual entry in cell D3 look like this:

cell D3: @NPV(D5,D7...D11)

Instead of entering the interest rate directly into the formula, which could have been done, the researcher here simply referenced cell D5, where the interest rate was already entered. If the value in D5 were changed—that is, if the researcher entered a different interest rate—then cell D3 would calculate a different value. The range in the formula was identified as D7..D11, which means that the values in cells D7 to D11, inclusive, were used.

When you look at the spreadsheet grid on a computer screen, however, you will not see the formula. It's "behind the scenes," so to speak: The researcher sees only the numbers produced by these formulas, without the complicated algebra. This is the true beauty of spreadsheets. To see the underlying formula in this spreadsheet, you would select cell D3; then, in the upper left corner of the screen, just above the spreadsheet grid, you would see the net present value formula. The (CO) stands for currency format with zero decimal places:

D3: (CO)   @NPV (D5,D7..D11)

	A	B	C	D	E
1					
2					
3		Net present value:		$7,321	
4					
5		Discount rate:		12.00%	
6					
7		Year 1:		(10,000)	
8		Year 2:		(6,000)	
9		Year 3:		500	
10		Year 4:		12,000	
11		Year 5:		23,000	
12					
13					
14					
15					

POWERFUL MATH FUNCTIONS

Built-in calculations like @NPV represent one of the most powerful features of spreadsheet programs. You simply need to know the exact format necessary to use each function, and you have tremendous power to manipulate information. Here are some common financial formulas:

Present Value: @PV(pmt,int,term) determines the present value of an even stream of payments (one in which all the payments are of the same size), technically an ordinary annuity (in which payments fall at end of the year). Requires the amount of each payment (pmt), a discount interest rate (int), and the range of values (range). To convert the formula to an annuity due, use:

@PV(pmt,int,term)*(1+int)

Note: some advanced versions of spreadsheet software allow for the entry of an annuity type–0 for ordinary annuity and 1 for an annuity due.

Future Value: @FV(pmt,int,range) determines the future value of an even stream of payments (one in which all the payments are of the same size), technically an ordinary annuity (in which payments fall at the end of the year). Requires the amount of each payment (pmt), an interest rate (int), and the range of values (range). To convert the formula to an annuity due, use:

@FV(pmt,int,term)*(1+int)

Payment: @PMT(prin,int,term) determines the amount of an amortized payment, as for a loan, given the present value or amount of the loan—technically an ordinary annuity (in which payments are made at the end of the year). Requires the initial amount or principal (prin), the interest rate (int), and the number of payment terms (term). To convert the formula to an annuity due, use:

@PMT(prin,int,term)/(1+int)

Net Present Value: @NPV(int,range) determines the present value of an uneven stream of payments (in which payments can vary in size). Requires a discount interest rate (int), and a range of values (range).

Internal Rate Of Return Or Irr: @IRR(guess,range) determines the interest rate that equates to a specific investment and resultant cash flow. Requires an initial guess at an interest rate (guess). Because the computer has to find an interest rate that fits the numbers, it performs an iterative mathematical process. Your guess at an interest rate assists the computer in quickly finding the correct rate. Required also is a range of values (range), of which often the first must be the initial investment, which is usually shown as a negative number. Check your software manual.

Number Of Years: @CTERM(int,fv,pv) determines the number of years or compounding periods of a loan, given an interest rate (int), a future value (fv), and the present value (pv). This formula solves for the compounding (C) terms (TERMs) with the other information known. There is also the function @TERM, which determines the number of years required to accumulate a given future value at a given interest rate and a given even stream of payments.

Simple Present and Future Values

Simple present and future values usually do not have a built-in formula. (I don't know why, perhaps because it's so simple, it's beneath the computer.) That is, if you wanted to find the future value of $10,000 in ten years earning 8% interest, you would need to enter the actual formula into a cell yourself, which is: $(1 + i)^n$. In a spreadsheet, you could reference other cells where the interest rate and the number of years were, rather than entering the values yourself.

For a *simple future value* enter the formula: $(1 + i)^n$ where i is the interest rate and n is the number of years.

For *simple present value* enter the formula: $1/((1 + i)^n)$ where i is the interest rate and n is the number of years.

Most spreadsheets recognize the following symbols for math:

+ or - for addition and subtraction

* or / for multiplication and division

^ for an exponent, as in $(1 + i)^5$, which means $(1 + i)^{\wedge 5}$

Curiously, although there is a function, @SQRT, for the square root, there is no preset function to find higher roots such as the cube root or the 5th root. To overcome this shortcoming, simply use fractional exponents. This standard algebraic form is usually accepted by spreadsheets. For instance, if you wanted to insert this expression into a spreadsheet:

$$\sqrt[5]{y}$$

The fifth root is equivalent to a fractional exponent of one-fifth. Algebraically, it would look like this:

$$y^{\frac{1}{5}}$$

Thus, you would enter:

$$y^{(1/5)}$$

For a simple square root, you could also use the exponent of 1/2.

STATISTICAL FUNCTIONS

A number of statistical functions are also built in, such as the average and standard deviation of a series of values. The basic calculations are:

Average: @AVG(list) determines the average of a series of values (list) which is the range of numbers identified by cell (B3:B12).

Standard Deviation: @STD(list) determines one standard deviation for a series of values (list) identified by cell.

Maximum: @MAX(list) determines the highest value in the range of numbers.

Minimum: @MIN(list) determines the lowest value in the range of numbers.

Other Functions

For business applications, there's an increasing number of functions available. For accountants, depreciation is included, including variations such as straight line, declining balance, and sum-of-the-year's-digits. Math functions often include logarithms, including natural logs. **Read through your manual carefully.**

ORGANIZING INFORMATION IN THE SPREADSHEET

If you're using complicated or involved spreadsheets, you'll want to organize them in a consistent manner. When a blank spreadsheet first appears on the screen, you may even want to have a generalized map prepared of where in the spreadsheet different types of information will go. You may want to identify, by cell address, your basic data, your data organized for reports, print macros, the location of certain formulas, or reference information.

ORGANIZING SPREADSHEETS BY SUBDIRECTORIES

Keeping spreadsheets by subdirectory can be useful in quickly finding which one you want. Subdirectories can be titled by subject, time-frame, organization, or even by name.

Give a spreadsheet a title that can be easily recalled later. Naming that spreadsheet 4C22T may have been a great idea at the time, but three months later such cryptic names can be a real puzzle. If you named it PROJ-4 as part of a budgets subdirectory, that name gives you an immediate idea of what it is. You might even want to keep a written log of spreadsheet titles when you have a multitude of them.

GRAPHS ARE POWER

Spreadsheet users tend to overuse graphs, especially those 3-D or exploding pie charts that can really catch readers' attention. People (like our bosses) do like them; just remember that you're trying to communicate a problem, a solution, a situation, or whatever, and a visual can have impact.

A suggestion: Focus on the core idea, or ideas, you're dealing with, and try to jazz up your spreadsheets with graphs. Often these graphs can be key parts of reports and presentations for other software. Take advantage of your ability to quickly prepare a variety of graphs, move them into reports, and to print them out on different paper and overhead-ready film.

TEN THINGS TO REMEMBER ABOUT SPREADSHEETS

1. Numbers in spreadsheets can lie. You may format a cell to show no decimal points, but the decimal information is still there! Other cells that reference that number will use all the exact value of the number, not the rounded value.

2. Print it out. Computers can go blank or freeze up, so always print out critical data.

3. Backup files. How many times have you heard this? A thousand times? This is the thousand-and-first time.

4. Make life easy for your report's readers (including you). Don't be lazy and neglect to format financial information with commas and dollar signs where appropriate. Trying to read numbers without commas is not only a challenge, it can produce mistakes.

5. Print your formulas. If you have carefully crafted complicated formulas, print them out. If your computer goes down, you don't want to have to reconstruct them.

6. Document your work for yourself. This is not only helpful to others; it can help you remember what you were thinking when you return to your work after a few years.

7. Lock 'em out. If others have access to your spreadsheets and you don't want them altered casually, use the program's password-protection function.

8. Don't forget Data Sort. Spreadsheets are versatile; the "data sort" function can alphabetize or sequence a column of numbers or words, saving you work. But be careful. This function can also alphabetize or sequence a column of numbers or words, undoing your work.

9. Zoom and splits. For expansive worksheets, use the program's ability to view separate parts on the screen at the same time. It assures consistency within the worksheet.

10. Be warned! The first time you use a newly constructed and complicated worksheet, assume that there's a glitch somewhere. There is.

WHAT-IFS—A SENSITIVE QUESTION

One of the most powerful features of spreadsheets is the ability to set up a problem and then to play What-Ifs. This process is often called *sensitivity analysis*, because it can show you how sensitive your end-result is to changes in a given variable. If an interest rate is increased or decreased by 2%, how much difference will it make in your finances in the end of the year?

You don't even need, in most cases, to know complicated math to set up such a spreadsheet. Just construct information as you would naturally think of it. Say you were studying the profitability of your company's products, and you wanted to know how a price change in a certain raw ingredient would change the company's bottom line. Set up a spreadsheet showing the costs as you generally think of them, from manufacturing through to retail. Include the percentage of various ingredients in each of your products, and build your spreadsheet up to cover all costs, and your bottom line. Make sure that the cost of each product is figured by referring to a master list of ingredient prices. Then, by changing the price of the ingredient you're studying, you can see the results for your company's profitability. The rate of change will tell you about the sensitivity of your company's bottom line to changes in ingredient costs.

MULTI-USE EXAMPLE: CRITICAL PATH

Spreadsheets can often substitute for more expensive specialized software. You just have to think about how to construct your spreadsheets. This doesn't mean you should reinvent the wheel when you don't have to—especially when off-the-shelf software can offer useful bells and whistles. But let's say you find yourself confronted with a project where you have to keep track of several things all at one time. You suspect you might get more projects like this in the future, so keeping track will not only help now, it will help you out in the future. A simple spreadsheet can do the trick.

DOING LOGS

In chapter 9, on algebra, we promised to show you how to solve the basic logarithm problem. For instance, in the expression $3^3 = 27$, the exponent is known (it's 3). But if the exponent isn't known, as in the expression $3^x = 27$, how can you figure out its value? Logs!

Here's the formula:

$$@log(a)/@log(b) \quad \text{or} \quad @ln(a)/@ln(b)$$

In the formula, a is the number and b is the base. You can use either the regular log function, @log, or the natural log function, @ln. In our problem, which requires us to solve for x in the equation $3^x = 27$, 27 is a, the number, and 3 is b, the base:

$$@log(27)/@log(3)$$

Our answer is 3. If the base is 10, as in the problem $10^x = 100{,}000$, then you simply use the function:

$$@log \text{ (number)}$$

Spreadsheets—Data Democracy

Spreadsheets allow us to analyze and solve problems today that were solvable in the past only with rules of thumb (well-developed approximating techniques). Because of the advances in computing power, you and I can now perform on our PC tasks that were once monumental even for the central data processing department. All thanks to the spreadsheet (and the Intel chip).

It's fitting that the people who created spreadsheets did not refer to using a spreadsheet as programming, even though spreadsheet use really is a kind of user-friendly programming. The term "programming" would have been a put-off to many potential customers. Instead, the spreadsheet is now seen as a sophisticated modern computing instrument that gives us, as individuals, the most powerful analytical tool available to anyone.

Stretch Yourself

16

WHAT IS LINEAR THINKING?

What's the alternative?

Math is the neural lubricant of advanced thinking in finance, economics, marketing, manufacturing, and other aspects of business. To help you stretch yourself, here are, in alphabetical order, a number of topics to get those neurons hopping:

Black-Sholes Option-Pricing Formula

Calculus

Chaos Theory and Fractals

Fuzzy Logic

Games and Strategies

Linear Programming

Markov Analysis

Queuing

S-Curves

BLACK-SHOLES OPTION-PRICING FORMULA

Professional investors want to know how to price an option (a fancy financial contract that allows an investor to buy or sell an underlying investment). IBM stock, for instance, would be the underlying investment, whereas an option on IBM stock would be the contract in question. A sophisticated investor only needs to invest in an option, which costs a fraction of the stock, to control that stock. That's leverage at its best.

In essence, the *Black-Sholes Option-Pricing Formula* calculates the present value of volatility values. The key to an option model is the volatility of the stock, a measure of its erratic fluctuation in price. Actually, the company (IBM) is immaterial to the option formula, which at first is hard to grasp. IBM stock is just an example of a commodity that has volatility and value. The formula doesn't care that it's Big Blue; it just wants to know the measure of the volatility of the stock.

The Black-Sholes formula was initially designed for European-style options, which can be exercised only at maturity, rather than American-style options, which can be bought and sold at any time up to their maturity, or expiration date. Modern option-pricing mathematical models have moved beyond the Black-Sholes formula to the binomial formula and variations of it. But Black-Sholes is the starting point, and if you wish to understand modern option-pricing, this is where you begin.

For the business executive, there is a crucial utility to these option-pricing models, because of the ubiquity of the executive stock option. Those are the financial goodies that some executives, and in a few cases many employees, have access to. A stock option allows its holder to purchase a share of stock at a fixed price. If the market price of the stock rises significantly above that fixed price, then the option-holder has the option of buying the stock at its fixed price and immediately selling it at its market price for a husky profit. The Black-Sholes formula and related models estimate the current value of the options based on an estimate of their future value.

As you read further and actually get into the math, be prepared to deal with Gordian-knot type math, a complicated mass of algebra that may seem overwhelming. It's worthwhile to persist.

SUGGESTED READING

For a comprehensive mathematical explanation:

Chriss, Neil A., *Black-Sholes and Beyond: Option-Pricing Models* (Chicago: Irwin, 1997).

For an in-depth primer on options and Black-Sholes:

Bookstaber, Richard M., *Option-Pricing and Investment Strategies* (Chicago: Probius, 1991).

FOR FURTHER BROWSING:

Type "black sholes model," without the hyphen, into your Web browser. You'll get some product information that may be helpful.

CALCULUS

There's really no need to be uptight about calculus. It's just another way of calculating things. Adding and subtracting are the most basic of calculations, followed by multiplying and dividing, and then powers and roots. Finally, there's the calculus, with its two opposite calculations, the derivative and integral. From kindergarten through high school, we grow up each year with more complicated math, reaching the edge of adulthood with calculus.

The derivative and integral are essentially opposites. The acts of performing these calculations are called differentiation and integration. Both were roughly known for hundreds of years, but it was Isaac Newton and Gottfried Liebniez, in the late 1600s, who at about the same time perceived that these two calculations, like multiplying and dividing, were indeed opposite calculations.

Each is so powerful that it's safe to say that the greatest engineering feats of the last 100 years would not have been possible without them. We never would have gotten to the moon—in fact, we couldn't have even hit it. You see, understanding the spin of the earth, coordinated with the movement of the moon, is well beyond the power of adding and multiplying.

So why do so many people fret over calculus? In my opinion, it's because it's taught in such a laborious nature by people who are basically math techies. Students are led blindly through a labyrinth of mathematical proofs, and battered with arcane math ideas like continuity and limits. They don't know why they're learning this stuff. They get bored, confused, unsurprisingly often just give up. It's like a hazing process.

I've always thought that instructors should first give students an overview, to demonstrate through examples what calculus is all about, and what it can do. Only then should classes bother with the mathematical niceties. I've sometimes imagined instructors muttering to themselves, "I suffered to learn this stuff. Now it's your turn."

In general, the *derivative* calculates rates of change, while the *integral* calculates the area under curves. Both are powerful for engineering, science, economics, and many applications in business.

The reason I became so fascinated with math at an early age, and with calculus in particular, was those exotic symbols! Some kids had murder mysteries or UFOs to worry about. I had those deliciously mysterious symbols that played on my imagination.

Some of my favorites:

$\sum$ Symbol for summation of a series

$\int$ Symbol for an integral

∂ Symbol for a partial derivative

$\prod$ Symbol for product of a series

Put together, they form an exotic symphony for the mind:

$$\int_a^b \sum_1^\infty f(x)dx \qquad\qquad \prod_{i=1}^n \left(\sum_{k=1}^n a_{ik}^2 \right)$$

$$\frac{\partial w}{\partial x} = \frac{2x}{x^2 + 2y^2} \qquad\qquad \sigma_{tp} = \sqrt{\sum_i^n \sum_j^n x_i x_j \sigma_i \sigma_j p_{ij}}$$

Change is simply the difference between one time frame and another. But the rate of change, which the calculus deals with, is the speed of that change.

Applications abound for business, in economics, marketing, engineering, manufacturing, and so forth. So if you've never dipped your toe in, now's a good time to do so. Try these sources:

FOR FURTHER READING:

Pick a textbook that you feel comfortable with, or take a community college class in calculus.

FOR FURTHER BROWSING:

www.forum.swarthmore.edu

CHAOS THEORY AND FRACTALS

CHAOS AND COMPLEXITY

There is no easy definition of chaos theory. What is chaos? Chaos is random movement, like that of leaves falling from a tree, like the hustle and bustle of pedestrians on a busy sidewalk, like the interactions of wind and temperature that form our weather patterns, or like stock market trades involving many thousands of individuals and institutions on a daily basis.

Are these really random movements? On closer examination, we might discover that these seemingly chaotic individual actions are only very complex—so complex, in fact, that we don't see the patterns until we explore them in detail, or step back to see the forest rather than the trees.

Consider what we typically call linear thinking. In economics, we might say that there are a number of forces at work: inflation, business cycles, employment and unemployment, interest rates, consumer confidence, productivity, and so forth. A model of the economic world should include these variables. If they are put together just right, our model might mirror the real economy. We could then have a model that replicates real life.

But what is the traditional way of analyzing the economy? We extract one or two items and see how they affect each other. Let's say we focus on the relationship between unemployment and inflation. We take these two items and we analyze and relate them. We have actually made an assumption of independence by separating them from the rest of the variables in the economy. That is, we are saying that we can actually see a one-to-one relationship between these two variables, independent of all the other variables.

This is an example of linear thinking: developing an independent algorithm for these two variables and treating them as a separate model. But what if the nation's productivity increases, or the government starts spending more money, or foreign imports increase, or the labor movement is quieted? What if all these things are happening at the same time, and each factor has an effect on all of the others?

That's called the real world. And although it has a chaotic feel to it, hopefully, for our sanity, we can discern some patterns in it. Chaos theory, then, might be a snappy way of saying "a theory of complexity."

Chaos theory represents an attempt to understand and explain complex relationships between many variables in a seemingly random system. If we can, we won't call it chaos, just complexity. That's the opposite of linear thinking; thinking in complex systems.

There is actually a field of mathematical study called "complex systems." *Complexity* here refers to the study of how complex behavior can generate simple behavior, whereas *chaos* refers to the study of how simple behavior can generate complex behavior. No matter how they're defined, chaos and complexity are inexorably intertwined.

FRACTALS

Have you seen those circular or spiral patterns on some computer screens? They're called fractals.

Fractals are repeating geometric designs that look surreal. They're part and parcel of chaos theory. These little geometrical patterns, not very impressive or interesting by themselves, when repeated over and over again yield unusual and sometimes spectacular designs. Order seems to emerge from chaos, and large designs within the fractal patterns are repeated within the pattern on a minute scale.

We should also mention the *butterfly effect*. It's the outrageous but seriously proposed idea that the tiny wind currents produced by the fluttering wing of an individual butterfly in the middle of the Amazon could initiate a series of causally connected events that could result in a hurricane in the Atlantic. A somewhat preposterous idea, certainly, but inspiring in that little events here and there can lead eventually to something much bigger. Perhaps that leaf falling in my front yard cause a slight movement of air that, added to the wind of a bumblebee's flight across town, triggered a series of events that grew into a gentle breeze, if not a hurricane.

FOR FURTHER READING:

James Gleick, *Chaos* (New York: Penguin, 1987).
Hans Lauwerier, *Fractals* (Princeton: Princeton University Press, 1991).
Edward Lorenz, *The Essence of Chaos* (Seattle:University of Washington Press, 1993).

FOR FURTHER BROWSING:

http://amath.colorado.edu/appm/faculty/jdm/faq.html

FUZZY LOGIC

What's "fuzzy" to an engineer may be simple common sense to us. Consider the following statement: "Jeremy is smart." We accept the statement as meaningful. That is, we have a general sense of what "smart" means and we accept, until proved wrong, that Jeremy is such a person.

However, to the engineer, this statement causes a problem. Jeremy's intelligence can only be classified by I.Q. or some other measurable, quantitative standard. The engineer needs to know that, say, Jeremy has an I.Q. of 150, or he got 1600 on the GMAT, or he's a member of Mensa. In the world of engineering or mathematics, something is either true or false, or quantifiable in some way.

Suppose you've been asked to select several people for a project team to work on a difficult problem. What you need is smart people. Your job is to select people from within the organization to work on this problem. Our common sense would tell us to look around, check personnel files, talk to people who know the organization, and start interviewing those potential workers.

As you interview, you may ask how the person scored on some tests, but we probably concentrate on questions that are not too quantifiable: "What are some of the problems you've solved, and how have you approached those problems?" "Why do you think this problem can be solved?" "Do you work well within a group, or are you primarily an individual contributor?" "How are problems generally solved?" You're trying, through your experience and knowledge, to get at the smartness ability of people.

Fuzzy doesn't mean "out of focus," in the way that a slide projector can be out of focus, so that we can't make out the picture. "Fuzzy," in our sense, means not expressible in binary or quantitative data. One early technical application of this kind of thinking was the operation of a cement kiln. Operators knew a number of general rules from experience, like "If the oxygen percentage is rather high and the free-lime and kiln-drive torque rate is normal, decrease the flow of gas and slightly reduce the fuel rate." This is one of about fifty different rules of thumb the operators use successfully.

Other applications include information-retrieval systems, controllers for robot arc-welders, and automatic navigational systems. They are frequently called expert systems, because they are attempts to duplicate artificially the behavior of experts in a certain field. These systems are also generally called "expert systems."

Perhaps the best way to think of fuzzy logic is as an attempt to duplicate human logic as nearly as possible.

FOR FURTHER READING:

Check operations research texts or quantitative management texts.

FOR FURTHER BROWSING:

www.cs.cmu.edu/groups/AI/html/faqs/ai/fuzzy/part1/faq
(Carnegie Mellon University)

GAMES AND STRATEGIES

Some people think of business as a game, and fail to take it seriously. Others, however, who take business very seriously, have learned that strategies derived from our pastimes of bridge, checkers, chess, and poker, not to mention the hard-core Las Vegas stuff, can provide us with tools that apply to the business world.

A game in its pure sense is about winning. We try to figure out the best strategy within the rules, and the best way to out-think our opponents, in order to win. We learn the rules to find the angles, and we study human nature to find weaknesses. Whether it's chess or contract negotiations, the rules of the game and human nature are equally critical.

The study of strategies applicable to any situation is called *game theory*. Game theory terminology includes such terms as *zero-sum*, *saddle points*, *mixed strategies*, and *dominance*.

There is, however, a major problem with game theory in its application to business. That's our inability to fill in the precise values in a payoff matrix. A payoff matrix is a kind of flowchart that includes all the possible outcomes for each player in a game, and assigns each outcome a value according to how desirable that outcome is to a player. If we knew these values exactly, the rest would be easy. But not all outcomes can be reduced to numbers. There may be outcomes whose consequences are uncertain and confusing to either party. The best we can do is often to rank one alternative over another.

To its credit, game theory does sharpen our ability to deal with the tough business world. The study of aggressive and even hostile players can better prepare us for the rough-and-tumble world.

FOR FURTHER READING:

Check operations research texts or quantitative management texts.

FOR FURTHER BROWSING:

Type "game theory" into your Web browser.
www.orie.cornell.edu/ (click on Michael Trick's Operations Research Page)

LINEAR PROGRAMMING

Above all, linear programming deals with optimum solutions. Your company has a number of products, a number of production plants, and a number of distribution centers. You, as the senior executive in charge of everything, want to know the optimum mix of products, plants, and distribution centers. It's time for some linear programming.

Linear programming can be mathematically described as the simultaneous solving of a group of one-dimensional equations. The solution is the most profitable of all the possible combinations. Technically, this is called the *optimization process*.

Consider this simple type of business problem that tries to find the best allocation of the firm's limited resources. It's the kind of problem that most texts on this subject deal with in chapter one:

Situation: A company produces two products, file cabinets and desks, which must be processed through two machines. Machine 1 can be operated for sixty hours per week, while machine 2, which requires some down-time, can be only operated for forty-eight hours. To produce a file cabinet takes four hours of machine 1's time and two hours of machine 2's time. To produce a desk takes two hours on machine 1 and four hours on machine 2. We make a profit of $6 for each file cabinet and $8 for each desk.

Problem: What is the optimum combination of file cabinets and desks we can produce to maximize our profit?

We assume that we are not going to go out and buy new machines or add other products. That is, we are constrained to the machines and products that we presently have.

We develop formulas such as:

$6F + $8D = profits (F for file cabinets and D for desks)

$4F + 2D \leq 60$ hours of machine 1 (that's less than or equal to 60 hours)

$2F + 4D \leq 48$ hours of machine 2

These are linear equations—that is, a linear proportion exists between the variables.

This system of equations can be resolved by solving the equations simultaneously, or by representing the equations graphically:

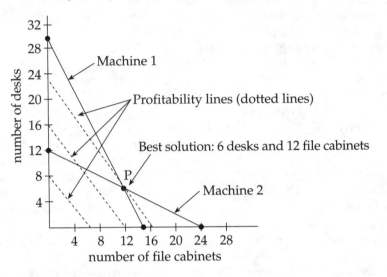

Point P shows the maximum profit, which turns out to be 6 file cabinets and 12 desks.

As you might expect, most companies have more complex situations, perhaps 25 different products and 10 different machines. To solve these problems, the *simplex method* was devised. In the simplex method, the multiple equations are solved through an iterative process using matrix algebra.

A matrix is a rectangular array of numbers in large parentheses. The horizontal numbers are referred to as rows and the vertical numbers are columns. (A determinant is a similar-looking array of numbers, but is bracketed by straight lines.) A matrix looks like this:

$$\begin{pmatrix} 1 & 7 & 9 & 4 \\ -4 & 3 & 3 & 0 \\ 0 & 5 & 5 & 1 \\ 5 & -2 & 1 & 8 \end{pmatrix}$$

FOR FURTHER READING:

Saul Gass, *An Illustrated Guide to Linear Programming* (New York: Dover Publications, 1970).

www.mcs.anl.gov/home/otc/guide/faq
   ftp://rtfm.mit.edu/pub/usenet/sci.answers/linear-programming.faq

MARKOV ANALYSIS

Markov analysis is a method of analyzing current action or movements of a variable to predict future actions or movements. It was developed in the early 1900s by the Russian mathematician A. Markov, who studied gas particles in a closed container. His method has since been applied especially to marketing.

Suppose, for example, you live near three book stores: Barnes and Noble, Borders, and a local book store that has just added a coffee bar. During a certain month, one store lost 100 customers, another gained 300, and the third gained 200.

On closer observation, however, there was more activity than these simple increases and decreases indicate. The table below shows a hypothetical complex movement of customers. A store that commissioned such a study would then design its promotional campaign on an understanding of these intricate movements of customers.

Number of customers				
	June	Gains	Losses	July
Store A	5,000	350	450	4,900
Store B	4,800	525	225	5,100
Store C	1,600	225	25	1,800

With such information, using probabilities in matrix algebra form, a store can make an effort to predict future market shares, predict rates of gains and losses, and analyze promotional campaigns and services.

The key ingredient is, of course, accurate information. A company can use its own customer data, as well as an outside marketing research firm that would, through surveys, estimate brand loyalties and store strengths and weaknesses. That data can then be used to perform this type of mathematical analysis.

FOR FURTHER READING:

Check operations research texts or quantitative management texts.

FOR FURTHER BROWSING:

Type "Markov analysis" into your Web browser.
www.orie.cornell.edu/ (click on Michael Trick's Operations Research Page)

QUEUING

It's not hard to find lines, or as the British would say, *queues*. We seem to stand in them all too often. A.K. Erlang, a Danish engineer, studied telephone facilities and automatic dialing equipment in the early 1900s. His work has been translated to apply to simple and complex queuing business situations.

A checkout counter in a supermarket is as good an example as any.

Suppose we'd like to know at what point customers feel dissatisfied enough to leave the store, or decide they'll hesitate to return, or tell their friends to avoid the store because of long lines.

The goal is to tell a business how best to solve queuing difficulties. Beyond the obvious fixes, like adding more counters and hiring more checkers, there are alternatives. Flexible use of personnel is important. Express checkout counters in grocery stores have been a solution for customers with small numbers of items. The store does a balancing act between additional expenditures and the loss of customers. Studying how competition copes with this problem is also important.

Queuing provides a mathematical model of what happens in a "waiting" line. Besides the actual math, charts are used, giving visual pictures of the situation:

Solid line represents time being served
Dotted line represents waiting time

Business applications are in customer service, fast-food restaurants, and manufacturing, among others.

FOR FURTHER READING:

Check operations research texts or quantitative management texts.

FOR FURTHER BROWSING:

Type "queuing theory" into your Web browser.
   www.orie.cornell.edu/   (click on Michael Trick's Operations Research Page)

S-CURVE

It looks roughly like a forward-leaning capital S, and is also called an *S-shaped curve*. More technically, it may be referred to as the *logistic* or *Pearl-Reed curve*.

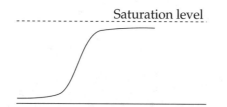

Saturation level

It represents growth, such as the sales growth of new products. Typically, a new product has an initial period of slow growth as the public learns about it, then (with any luck) a period of rapid growth as sales spread throughout the economy, and finally, the inevitable slowdown as sales reach their saturation point.

The S-curve could represent many growth situations, such as the start-up and growth of a new industry or the leaning curve of a new employee learning the ropes.

The general formula for the curve is:

$$y = \frac{a}{1 + be^{-cx}}$$

e is approximately 2.71828

FURTHER READING:

Check a business statistics text. The S-curve is usually found in one of the later chapters.

17

Glossary

abscissa In graphing, the horizontal distance from the y-axis to a point. See *ordinate*.

absolute value The numerical, or positive, value of a number or expression. It is written with bars before and after the number. A negative number is thus converted to its positive counterpart. For instance, the absolute value of -4 is 4. In computer spreadsheets, it is a reference to an exact cell, not a relative cell. In a spreadsheet, the cell reference is often written with dollar signs before the number and letter of the cell.

actuary A mathematician specializing in insurance or pensions. Actuaries deal with mortality tables (the number of persons who die at different ages), probability, and present and future value calculations.

algebra Math that uses letters or symbols to represent numbers or values for a general case. Algebra also has rules for the manipulation of the values. For instance, the general case for determining the future value of an investment, or any future value, is:

$$FV = PV(1 + i)^n$$

Each letter or group of letters represents a value. In this formula the two letters FV represent the future value and PV the present value. Only the one letter i is designated to represent the interest rate and n the number of years. Other people may use other letters or combinations of letters to represent the general values.

Because of algebraic rules, you can solve for any value in this formula by manipulating the formula. For instance, if you knew the value for future value (FV) but wanted to find the value for present value (PV), you could either enter all the numbers except for the unknown PV and do the arithmetic, or you could rearrange the formula for easy solving. Rearranging the formula allows you to more easily find the value you are seeking. To rearrange this formula using the rules of algebra you could divide each side of the equation by $(1 + i)^n$ giving you the new form of:

$$PV = \frac{FV}{(1+i)^n}$$

This then allows you insert the values you know. See *formula*.

algorithm A step-by-step mathematical or problem-solving procedure.

amortize A financial mathematical method of paying equal amounts to pay off a loan or other financial obligations. An example is a mortgage. A conventional thirty-year mortgage requires the exact same payment for all thirty years. Although the amount of the interest and principal represented in each payment changes during the thirty years, the actual payment to the bank or mortgage company is the same. This is in contrast to a car loan, the payments for which may decline over the thirty-six months, or however long it's for, as the principal is paid down. See *mortgage*.

analysis The application of common sense along with mathematical and statistical calculations to describe, understand, contrast, hypothesize, solve, and make decisions about a problem.

analytical geometry Geometry primarily using algebraic expressions defined in terms of position coordinates on a graph.

annualized or effective rate To take any rate given in a certain time frame and convert it to a rate for the year.

When Rip-Off Retailers offered a "low, low" interest rate of only 2 percent, Marty was quick to point out that it was a monthly rate and that the *annualized rate* would be 26.82 percent—no bargain.

annuity In financial calculations, a stream of usually equal payments that are paid out, such as a pension. The payments can be variable or increasing. It can also refer to paying in on an equal amount, such as buying an annuity with monthly payments. If money is paid in or out at the beginning of the period, say monthly, it is called an *annuity due*. If money is paid in or out at the end of the period it is called an *ordinary annuity*.

approximation The process of guessing or ball-parking a number rather than precisely calculating it.

arithmetic The mathematics of addition and subtraction and multiplication and division. It does not generally denote the more complex forms of mathematics such as calculus.

arithmetic progression See *geometric progression*

assumptions A variable, or parameter, in a mathematical or statistical argument. For example, the amount of inflation, unemployment and productivity could be assumptions in an economic model. See *parameter*.

average (mean) The value obtained by adding each value and dividing by the number of values. See *median* and *mode*.

bar graph See *graphs*.

base 10 Our number system involves 10 symbols, which are added to and repeated for numbers over 10. Thus, it is said we have a number system to the base 10. If our number system was to the base 4, the system would have four symbols and would look like: 0, 1 ,2 ,3, 10, 11, 12, 13, 20, 21, 22, 23, 30, 31, 32...and so forth.

basis point One-hundredth of one percent. For instance, if treasury bonds are paying 7.50 percent interest, an increase to 7.51 percent is said to increase by one basis point. An increase to 7.60 percent would be an increase of 10 basis points, and to 8.50 percent would be 100 basis points.

Bayes' Theorem A statistical method by which the number of false positives are estimated. This is especially true for procedures that are not 100 percent precise. Thomas Bayes was a minister in England in the 1700s.

bell-shaped curve The most common curve in statistics. It represents the ideal distribution. It is sometimes called the *normal curve* or *normal distribution*. There are surprisingly many examples of bell-shaped type distributions in nature, business, and everyday activities.

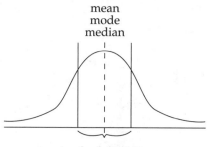

mean
mode
median

standard deviation

bias A statistical concept that deals with pure information. If a pollster asks questions that are nonobjective, the results can be biased, or slanted.

binary A number system using only two symbols, commonly 1 and 0. It is used as the basis of computer logic.

bimodal distribution A statistical distribution in which there are two peaks, or modes, of data, in contrast to the typical bell-shaped curve, which has only one peak.

binomial A mathematical or algebraic expression of two terms connected by a plus or minus sign. An example of a binomial is $3x + 4y$. A monomial has one term, such as $5xy$. A trinomial has three terms, such as $6x + 7y + 8z$. Any algebraic expression of more than two terms is called a polynomial.

binomial formula (or theorem) The rule for the expansion of the power of a binomial.

Black-Sholes formula A complicated mathematical formula to determine the present value of options. This is the most common method of determining the present value of stock options given to company executives.

Boolean algebra or logic A mathematical logic based on two elements, 1 and 0, or true and false, and the operations of *and*, *or*, and *not*. It is the logic used in computers. George Boole was a British mathematician.

breakeven analysis; breakeven point The analysis of profits by determining the relationship between the costs and revenues. Often illustrated by a *breakeven graph*. In a simple breakeven graph the fixed costs are shown as a horizontal line, with the variable costs starting at the fixed costs and moving on an upward slope. That is, whereas fixed costs are flat (the cost of the basic factory), variable costs increase as more products are made (the costs of materials and labor). The revenue line increases from zero and eventually will cross the variable cost line, which at that point is called the breakeven point. After that point, profit is then made on all additional products. The real world is not this simple. In the real world each of the lines is not straight, but will have jumps and squiggles in it. But the simple graph gives the basic idea, onto which the real world is then imposed.

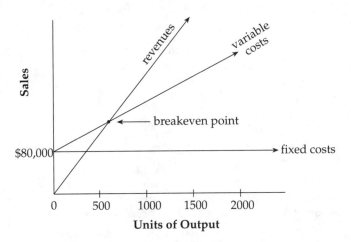

brownian motion or movement Random motion, originally referring to molecular movements, but now also referring to random motion observed in business activities, such as consumer buying habits.

calculator, use of Many business applications of mathematics only require a simple hand-held calculator, such as ratios, taxes, costs, and revenues. Some applications, such as financial calculations of present and future value, require a more substantial calculator, but these can still be small hand-held types. Only in more complicated applications, such as statistics or spreadsheets, are computers necessary.

calculus An advanced method of calculation based on the rate of change. There are two methods that are the opposite of each other, called the *derivative* and the *integral*. The process of finding the derivative is called *differentiation*; finding the integral is known as *integration*. Just as there are the paired and opposite calculations of addition and subtraction, multiplication and division, so there is the paired calculations of differentiation and integration. A typical derivative calculates the minimum or maximum of a formula, whereas a typical integral calculates the area under a curve. These two calculations allow for complex and useful calculations in engineering, science, and business. The discovery of the calculus in the late 1600s was made by two mathematicians, Isaac Newton and Gottfried Leibniz.

cardinal number A number that represents the magnitude of a quantity but not the order of that quantity. This is in contrast to an ordinal number, which sets its order as well as its magnitude.

cause-and-effect diagram A graphic technique showing the results of alternatives. It also is known as the *fishbone diagram*, because it looks like the skeleton of a fish.

certainty In probability, the concept that something is certain to happen. In a race, it is certain there will be a winner, and in a coin toss it is certain that either heads or tails will result (as long as the coin doesn't land on its edge).

chaos theory A new mathematical method still in its developmental stage that involves complicated real-life applications. Predicting weather patterns is an example of it.

chart See *graph*.

chi square test A statistical test comparing the frequencies of two distributions to see if they are alike or not. It helps decide whether a sample distribution could be a random sample from that population. Written as χ^2, is named from the Greek letter chi. To use the results, the degrees of freedom of the sample must be known. The degrees of freedom is usually the number of observations minus one (since you are calculating with one of the variables leaving the number that remains). A table usually called the *values of* χ^2 is consulted. See *statistics*.

circle A perfect round curve with all points equally distant from the center.

coefficient The numerical part of an algebraic expression such as 4x.

coefficient of determination In statistics, it is also know as r². See *r²*.

complex expression or number A number or expression that includes an imaginary number.

compound interest Interest that itself earns interest during a period. For instance, if $1,000 was invested for one year at 5 percent compounded monthly, then it would earn interest monthly not only on the initial $1,000 but on the interest it earned. In this case the total investment at the end of the year would be $1,051. This is in contrast to simple interest, which has no compounding during the year. If the $1,000 earned 5 percent simple interest, then the value of the investment at the end of the year would be simply $1,050 or 5 percent greater.

compounding The process of earning interest on interest. See *compound interest*.

computer, use of There are many applications of the computer to math, statistics, and business in general. Spreadsheets and databases are two of the most common uses for the math-oriented business person.

commutative law Multiplying a x b is equal to multiplying b x a. See *distributive law*.

concave and convex curves In graphing, a concave curve looks like one of the arches of McDonald's, or the entrance to a cave or mine. The curve can be a pure arch or concave upwards or downwards. This is in contrast to convex, which is a curve shaped like a big U.

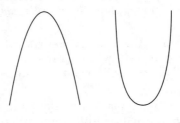

concave   convex

confidence interval In statistics, the level at which the results are acceptable. The most commonly used is the 95 percent confidence interval.

congruent Two things that are exactly equal. Often used in geometry, it means coinciding exactly when superimposed. As in, triangle A is congruent to triangle B, which means that the sides and angles of both triangles are exactly equal.

constant An unchanging value. In an algebraic formula a constant is often represented with the letter k. See *variable*.

convex See *concave and convex curves*.

correlation A similar relationship. For instance, if the Dow Jones average is up, chances are the S&P 500 is also up. This relation is said to be correlated positively. A negative correlation is often referred to as an inverse relationship. Correlation is measured between -1 for opposite correlation, 0 for no correlation, and +1 for perfect correlation. See *inverse*.

correlation coefficient See *r*.

cost of capital An overall investment rate a company uses to test if a project should be approved or not.

criterion A term used in spreadsheets to denote a parameter or an aspect of information.

cube (of a number)   The result of multiplying a number by itself three times. 9 is the cube of 3 (3 x 3 x 3 equals 9).

cubed root   A factor of a number that when cubed (multiplied by itself three times) equals the number. For instance, 3 is the cubed root of 9.

decimal   A way of expressing fractions. 5 divided by 10 is .5, or *point 5*.

decision tree   A method in management decision-making that looks at all of the options and the resultant branching options. It is so named because it looks like a tree.

degrees of freedom   A statistical concept that usually refers to the number of data values in a sample. It is usually minus one because you are testing one of them, with the others remaining. See *chi square test*.

delta (Δ)   The mathematical notation for an incremental difference. It uses the Greek symbol delta.

denominator   The number or algebraic expression written below the line in a fraction. The numerator, or the *number* of parts to the whole, is above the line.

dependent variable   The variable in an algebraic formula that depends on the independent variable. It is the independent variable that "calls the shots" on the dependent variable. In an algebraic expression, the letter y is often the dependent variable.

derivative   One of two calculations in calculus. The other is the *integral*. See *calculus*.

determinant   An array of numbers arranged in rows and columns that has a numerical value. It is a method to solve simultaneous equations (those with similar unknowns). A determinant has straight lines to bracket the array of numbers. A matrix has numbers as well but does not itself equal a value. See *matrix*.

differentiation   The process of calculating one of two calculations of the calculus. The other process is *integration*. See *calculus*.

digit   One of our ten numbers, 0 through 9, because we have a number system to the base 10. If we had a number system based on 4, we would have four numbers or digits.

discount rate   The rate of interest, or investment, used in a present value calculation. See *present value*.

discounting   The process of determining present value.

discounted cash flow   Calculating the present value of a stream of payments, or cash flow. An interest rate (discount rate) is used to find the present value, thus the calculation is referred to as *discounting*.

dispersion   A statistical measurement of variability of data values. The standard deviation is the most common measurement of dispersion.

distributive law   Multiplying a x (b + c) is equal to multiplying a x b and multiplying it with c. See *commutative law*.

e A mathematical constant equaling 2.71828...(non-ending). It is very useful in formulas expressing growth rates, such as population, investments, or growth in nature. The Swiss mathematician Leonhard Euler saw the value of a special constant, which he named *e*. It is sometimes called *Euler's constant*.

effective rate See *annualized rate*.

ellipse An oval or egg-like geometric figure in which all points are equally distant from two points.

entropy A tendency or measurement of the state of disorder emerging from a state of order.

envelope The confines of a problem or situation. The phrase *push the envelope* means enlarging the confines or boundaries.

equation Two mathematical expressions set equal to each other and written with an equal sign between them.

exponent The number of times a number is multiplied by itself. It is often referred to as *raised to the power of*. In the expression 5^4, the exponent is 4 (or the number 5 is raised to the power of 4), meaning the number 5 is multiplied by itself 4 times, or 5x5x5x5 = 625.

exponential Refers to the use of exponents or powers.

F distribution or F ratio A statistical test between the *variances or standard deviations* of two distributions to see how alike they are or not. See *statistics*.

factorial (!) The product (multiplication) of every consecutive number up to and including the specified number. Written with an exclamation point. 4! equals 24 (1 x 2 x 3 x 4 = 24).

fair market value (FMV) Used in real estate, tax, and other applications, it refers to the market value, or the value someone is willing to pay. This is in contrast to the value the investment or real estate was originally bought for, or what the owner thinks the value should be.

fishbone diagram See *cause-and-effect diagram*

flow chart A detailed diagram showing the complete step-by-step process of manufacturing or some other process.

fraction A numerator divided by a denominator

formula An equation showing a mathematical relationship between things.

The formula for calculating the future value of a number is:
$$FV = PV(1 + i)^n$$
In this formula, FV stands for future value, PV for present value, i for the interest rate, and n the number of years of compounding. Using this formula, if you had $1,000 now, present value, and it could earn 7 percent designated by the

symbol i in the formula, and it would grow for 5 years
designated by the power of 5 in the formula, the answer
would be determined as follows:

$$FV = \$1,000 \times (1 + .07)^5$$
$$FV = \$1,000 \times (1.07)^5$$

(you'll probably like to use a calculator here, although you
can do it by hand — just multiply 1.07 by itself 4 more times
— because it is already multiplied by itself once)

$$FV = \$1,000 \times 1.4$$
$$FV = \$1,400$$

That is, the \$1,000 will grow to \$1,400 in 5 years.

---

future dollars   A value of an investment or quantity into the future.

future value (FV)   The value of something in the future. It could be the accumulation of a series of values, like our continual investing in a 401(k) plan, or the value of a CD in the future. The future value is calculated with an investment rate assumption. An example would be the value of investing \$2,000 into an IRA each year for twenty years with the assumption of an investment rate of 8 percent.   That future value is calculated to be approximately \$91,500. Calculating the future value is the opposite of calculating the present value. See *present value* and, for an illustration, see *formula.*

fuzzy logic   A new form of algebra that uses a range of values, from true to false. It is used in decision-making with imprecise information.   The outcome of fuzzy logic is the assignment of a value based on the probability that it is true.

game theory   The mathematical method of analyzing situations similar to games that people play where there is a winner and a loser. It is used in management decision-making.

Gantt chart   A work scheduling chart devised initially by Henry Gantt.

geometry   The mathematical study of points, lines, and shapes.

geometric mean   In financial and statistical calculations, the compounded rate of return.

geometric progression   A series of numbers where each term has a constant *multiplied* to it. This is in contrast to an arithmetic progression, where each term has a constant *added* to it. An example of a geometric progression is: 3, 6, 12, 24, 48... where each next term is multiplied by 2. An example of an arithmetic progression is: 3, 6, 9, 12, 15... where 3 is added to each next term.

Googol   Reportedly named by an infant, the googol is a 1 with 100 zeros behind it. In math circles, it is written as 10^{100}. It dwarfs the biggest numbers we normally think of, such as a billion or a trillion, which are only 10^9 and 10^{12}. A googolplex is even bigger, 10^{googol}.

graph or chart; graphing or charting The visual presentation of data in a way that gives clarity to the data. The common forms of graphs or charts are *line, bar,* and *pie.* Bar charts can be vertical or horizontal or presented in 3-D form, to represent three dimensions. More complex graphs can combine line and bar charts. A *pictogram* uses visual pictures for impact or to make a boring chart more interesting.

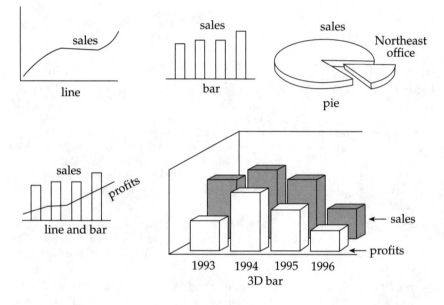

line

bar

pie

line and bar

3D bar

number of keys made

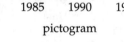

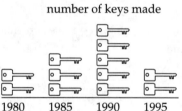

1980   1985   1990   1995

pictogram

Greek alphabet

Letters		Names	Letters		Name	Letters		Names
A	α	alpha	I	ι	iota	P	ρ	rho
B	β	beta	K	κ	kappa	Σ	σ	sigma
Γ	γ	gamma	Λ	λ	lambda	T	τ	tau
Δ	δ	delta	M	μ	mu	Y	υ	upsilon
E	ε	epsilon	N	ν	nu	Φ	φ	phi
Z	ζ	zeta	Ξ	ξ	xi	X	χ	chi
H	η	eta	O	o	omicron	Ψ	ψ	psi
Θ	θ	theta	Π	π	pi	Ω	ω	omega

hexadecimal Related to the number 16. The hexadecimal system of numbers uses 0 through 9, and then the letters A through F to represent the numbers 10 through 15. Computer programmers use the hexadecimal system because numbers can be written more compactly. The number 12 is 1100 in the binary system, but simply the letter C in the hexadecimal system.

histogram (frequency diagram) In statistics, a bar chart diagram that represents the frequency of data values, often roughly bell-shaped. It is a basic way to represent statistic data. The name derives from the Greek word *histos* for mast; thus it is a mast- or column-like bar chart.

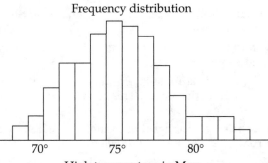

Frequency distribution

High temperature in May

hyperbola A mathematical curve.

hypothesis A tentative explanation or theory that requires further investigation.

imaginary number The square root of a negative. It is shown as *i*. Although this expression doesn't exist in normal numbers because a number squared is always positive, in advanced math a convention has developed to account for such nonexistent numbers. It is written with the radical or square root sign as:

$$i = \sqrt{-1}$$

independent variable   The variable that calls the shots, so to speak, in algebraic formulas. The dependent variable *depends* on the independent variable. In an algebraic expression the letter x is often the independent variable.

inequalities   A mathematical relationship in which one element is greater than or less than another. The symbol > is greater than, and the symbol < is less than. An example of an inequality expression is $2x > y$, meaning that twice the value of x is always greater than y. An inequality can include the equal sign as well, such as the expression $4x \geq y$, meaning that four times the value of x is always greater than or equal to y.

infinity (represented by the symbol ∞)   How do you say, so big that it is bigger than anything? As a mathematician would say, it is unbounded. It is a concept that mathematicians use, but it is beyond comprehension.

inflection point   A point on a graph where the curve, or line, changes direction.

integer   A whole number, as opposed to a decimal or fraction.

integral   One of two calculations in calculus. The other is the *derivative*. See *calculus*.

integration   The process of calculating one of two calculations of the calculus. The other process is *differentiation*. See *calculus*.

internal rate of return (IRR)   The rate of interest that discounts a stream of payments to a present value.

interest   In financial math, the amount of money earned by the principal, or the amount invested.

interval   In statistics, the determination of how to separate data values into ordered and sequenced data.

inverse   An opposite relationship. For instance, if interest rates increase, then the value of bonds decreases. This is an example of an inverse relationship. See *correlation*

irrational number   A number that cannot be created by a fraction, such as the square root of 2. See *rational number*

iteration   Repeating a calculation, usually with one variable changing each time.

kinetic energy   The energy an object has because of its speed.

kurtosis   A statistical measurement of how well data values bunch around the center of a distribution relative to the high and low values. It is also referred to as *peakedness*.

least-squares method   A statistical calculation of correlation. It is the method of summing the squared differences to a minimum, thus its name.

lemma   A subpart of a theory.

line graph   A common graph showing a line connecting the important points. See *graphs*.

linear A mathematical expression resulting in a straight line when graphed.

linear programming A mathematical method of finding the optimum or best solution to a problem. On a technical level, linear programming is the solving of linear equations. Business applications are in distribution systems, manufacture scheduling and the mix of products a company offers, among others.

logarithm The power, or exponent, of a mathematical expression. In the equation $100 = 10^2$, 2 is the logarithm of 100, to the base 10. We normally think of logarithms, when we think of them at all, to the base of 10. However, in mathematics, the base can be any number, including e, which is called the *natural logarithm*. It's called natural because it describes relationships often found in nature, such as the growth of bacteria.

logarithmic curve A nonlinear curve that uses logarithms.

lowest common denominator The smallest number to which all other numbers in a group can be changed.

Markov analysis A mathematical method of analyzing current movements to predict future movements. It is used for marketing analysis, among other applications. It is named for the Russian mathematician Andrei Andreevich Markov (1856-1922).

matrix In mathematics, a rectangular array of numbers, usually in large parentheses. The horizontal numbers are referred to as *rows* and the vertical numbers as *columns*. A similar-looking array of numbers, but very different, is called a *determinant*, which is bracketed by straight lines. A determinant equates to a value, whereas a matrix does not. See *determinant*.

matrix algebra (or matrix math) The specific order of arithmetic operations involving matrices, such as addition, subtraction, and multiplication. For instance, a matrix can be multiplied by a single number or another matrix. See *matrix*.

mean (average) Sometimes called the arithmetic mean, it is the value obtained by adding the values and dividing by the number of values. It is the most common of all statistical measurements. The mean of 4, 8, 8, 17, and 23 is 12: Adding the numbers and dividing by 5 equals 12. The mean is often represented in statistical formulas by x-bar, or a bar over an x:

$$mean = \overline{X}$$

median The midpoint of the data values. It's the number in the middle when three or more numbers are in sequential order. Just like the highway *median strip* divides the road, the median divides the value points. The median of 4, 8, 8, 17, and 23 is 8. If there is an *even* number of data values, then the average of the two number in the middle is the median. For instance, the median of 4, 8, 17, and 23 is 12.5 (8 + 17 equals 25 divided by 2 equals 12.5). See *mean* and *mode*.

mixed number A number made up of an integer and a fraction, such as $5\frac{1}{4}$.

mode The most common data value. The mode of 4, 8, 8, 17, and 23 is 8. See *mean* and *median*.

model A mathematical representation of a real process. If the model is valid it will represent and project useful values. Inherent in a model are assumptions and their relationships. A model of the economy could make certain assumptions about unemployment, inflation, and productivity and specify how each is related to one another. A model allows the running of *what ifs*, technically called *sensitivity analysis*. That is, it allows you to determine how sensitive each assumption is on the results of the model.

monte carlo simulation A trial and error method and random sampling used in market research.

mortgage An amortized loan typically over thirty years, although mortgages can be for shorter periods. Although the payments are equal, the amount of interest and principal changes during the thirty years. For instance, the beginning payments are mostly interest, which slowly declines to become mostly principal at the end of the mortgage term. See *amortize*.

multiple correlation or regression In statistics, comparing or correlating many variables to find which are correlated, if any. A simple correlation or regression compares just two variables.

natural logarithm See *e*.

net present value (NPV) The present value of an *uneven* stream of payments. This calculation occurs typically in the analysis of new business projects or ventures. For instance, in commercial real estate a new building is projected to show varying annual cash flows, at first some negative, but eventually mostly positive. To find the net present value of this uneven series, the present value of each payment must be individually calculated and then *netted*, or added together. In this process, negative as well as positive present values are combined. NPV is in contrast to determining the present value of a series of *equal* payments, such as annuities or pensions, where there are neat formulas to determine the entire present value in one calculation.

nominal The actual or named rate of interest. This is in contrast to a *real rate*, which is adjusted for inflation. See *real*.

normal curve; normal distribution The graph of a typical bell-shaped curve where the mean, mode and median are all the same. See *bell-shaped curve*.

null hypothesis An assumption made at the beginning of a statistical experiment that the results obtained are by chance only. The object of most statistical experiments is to find a reason for the results other than chance, and thus reject the *null hypothesis*. This *nullifies* the hypothesis of chance by proving that there is a cause or reason for the results. At first this appears to be a confusing double-negative to statistical newcomers, but it becomes understandable after working with specific problems. In math formulas, the null hypothesis is written as H_0 and the alternative nonchance hypothesis is written as H_1.

numerator   The number or algebraic expression written above the line in a fraction. It gives the *number* of parts of the whole. The denominator is below the line.

operations research   The application of mathematical methods to a variety of business problems.

opportunity cost; opportunity loss   The concept that all investment or business options have some risk, even those that seem the safest. The safest, like CDs, risk losing the opportunity of greater gains elsewhere. By investing in one project, a business cannot invest in another that could prove to be more profitable.

optimization   A term used in investment mathematics to find the right balance between the different asset classes, given an amount of risk taken.

ordinal number   A number that represents the order in a series as well as the magnitude of a quantity. This is in contrast to a *cardinal number*, which only represents its magnitude but not order.

ordinate   In graphing, the vertical distance from the x-axis to a point. See *abscissa*.

origin   In graphing it is the zero point. It is that point at the center or where the x-axis and y-axis meet.

outlier   In statistics, a data value that is far outside the normal range.

parabola   A common mathematical curve in algebra, where all oncoming lines reflect to a single point. It describes the curve of a satellite dish that captures television waves efficiently.

parameter   A variable or assumption in a mathematical or statistical argument. See *assumption*.

Pareto's rule (law or diagram)   The "80-20" rule, which suggests, for instance, that 80 percent of your business comes from 20 percent of your customers, or that 80 percent of your company's problem comes from 20 percent of its activities. It appears to be a common occurrence in business and life. It is named for Vilfredo Pareto, a nineteenth-century economist.

Pascal's triangle   A specific order of numbers in a triangular array devised by the French mathematician Pascal.

payback period   The period of time it takes to recover the initial cost of an investment.

percent   An amount expressed per 100. If twenty-five people of out 100 buy specials at a store, that is represented as 25 percent.

PERT diagram   An acronym for Program Evaluation Review Technique. It is a scheduling method showing the various activities on a project and the sequence of those activities to complete the task.

perpendicular   Lines that meet at 90°, or at right angles.

permutations   Possible arrangements in a specific order. The phrase *combinations and permutations* refers to all of the possible relationships and all of the specific relationships.

pi (π)   A mathematical constant equaling 3.14159...(non-ending). It is extremely useful in geometry. It equals the circumference of a circle divided by the diameter. It is represented by the Greek letter for p.

pie chart or graph   A circular graph, like a pie, showing divisions of items according to their frequencies. See *graphs*.

polynomial   See *binomial*.

population   A specific term in statistics that refers to the whole range of whatever is being studied, as opposed to a sample, which is only a part of the population.

power   The number of times a number is multiplied by itself. It is often referred to as *raised to the power of*. It is also referred to as the *exponent*. In the expression 5^4, the power (or exponent) is 4, meaning the number 5 is multiplied by itself 4 times, or 5 x 5 x 5 x 5 = 625.

present value (PV)   How much something in the future is valued today. It could be one value in the future or a series of values. With an interest rate assumption, called the discount rate, and the number of years, a value is determined today. An example is a zero-coupon bond, where the value today is the value of $1,000 at maturity. If the interest rate is 7 percent and is due in ten years, the value today will be about $500, or about one-half. This means if you invested the $500 today at 7 percent then after ten years you would have $1,000. See *future value*

present-day dollars   See *today's dollars*.

pricing   The analysis of pricing a product in the marketplace.

prime (number)   A whole number (not a fraction or decimal) only divisible by itself and 1. The number 1 is not considered a prime number. The numbers 2, 3, 5, and 7 are prime numbers, for instance. The number 4 can be divided by 2 equally, as can 6 and 8.

principal   In financial math, the amount invested.

probability   Mathematical method representing and analyzing whether specific events will happen or not. It is the likelihood of something happening. The probability of getting heads when flipping a coin is 50 percent (or written as a decimal .5).

product   The result of multiplication. Multiplying 4 and 5 results in the product 20.

projection   A mathematical or quantitative extension of known information into the future. For instance, if the inflation rate is currently 3 percent, a projection for inflation could be 3 percent, higher, or lower depending on the assumptions made.

Pythagorean theorem   The formula that specifies that the square of the hypotenuse (the long side of a right triangle) equals the sum of the squares of each other side:

$$c^2 = a^2 + b^2$$

quadratic equation A common mathematical expression that has the form:

$$ax^2 + bx + c = 0$$

quadratic formula The general mathematical expression to solve any quadratic equation.

quantity discounts By buying in bulk, or volume, a discount is usually available.

queuing theory A mathematical analysis of things that happen in a single line, such as in a queue (very British). Business applications are in manufacturing, customer service, and fast-food restaurants, among others.

quotient The result of division. The quotient of 14 (the dividend) divided by 2 (the divisor) is 7.

r (correlation coefficient) A measurement of how closely two variables are related to each other. For instance, how related is watching TV sitcoms and doing well in statistics? The value of 1 would mean a perfect fit, or correlation, the value of 0 would indicate no correlation, and -1 an opposite, or inverse, relationship. What is your guess? If 1, then it would mean the more sitcoms, the higher the stat grade (which we guess would not be the case). If 0, there would be no relation between the number of sitcoms watched and the grade. Finally, if -1, the more sitcoms the lower the stat grade (which is what we suspect).

r squared (r^2) A measurement of how closely the regression line fits the actual data, usually as shown on a scatter diagram (sometimes called scattergrams or scatterplots). Also know as the *coefficient of determination*.

radical sign ($\sqrt{}$) A mathematical sign indicating a root of a number. It usually shows the square root of a number.

random A nonorganized or nonsequential order or number. See *random number*

random number A number selected in an nonordered way. Statistics uses random numbers and random sampling to arbitrarily select people for a survey. Computers or tables can generate random numbers for such experiments.

range A simple statistical measurement of how far a distribution is dispersed. It is the difference between the maximum and minimum data values.

rational number A number obtained by dividing one whole number by another. For example, 3 divided by 5, written as $^3/_5$, is a rational number. Numbers that cannot be created by a fraction are called *irrational*.

ratio A fraction or relationship between two numbers. The P/E ratio (price/earnings) is the fraction of price divided by earnings. Business and investments use many ratios.

real In finance, a number adjusted for inflation. This is in contrast to a *nominal value*, which is the actual, or named, value. For instance, if an investment earns 5 percent interest but inflation takes away 3 percent, then the real interest rate is 2 percent. The nominal interest rate is 5 percent in this example, whereas the end result, or real, interest rate is only 2 percent.

reciprocal   The opposite, inverse, or reverse of a fraction. The reciprocal of 5 is 1 divided by 5. In algebraic terms, the reciprocal of a is 1 divided by a.

rectangles   A four-sided geometric figure with opposite sides equal. A four-sided figure without equal opposite sides is a *trapezoid*.

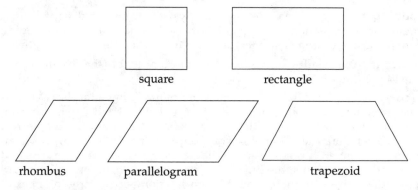

square   rectangle

rhombus   parallelogram   trapezoid

regression analysis   The analysis of how closely, or not, the data of a statistical experiment is related, or correlated.

regression line (least squares line)   The straight line that best fits or passes through the scatter diagram. The line then not only represents the data, but predicts it as the line is extended farther.

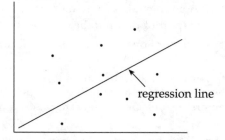

regression line

regression to the mean   In statistics, a statement that the sample will be similar to the whole population when the sample size is large enough. Tossing a coin, you might start with getting mostly heads or tails by chance, but if you keep tossing the coin you will eventually get close to an equal number of heads and tails. This is called regressing to the mean, meaning that after a while the tossing will approach the mean, or the average, of the population.

reorder points   An analysis of when to efficiently reorder materials for manufacturing with the minimum of storage.

right angle or triangle   A 90° angle or a triangle having one angle at 90⁰.

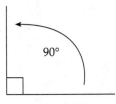

right angle

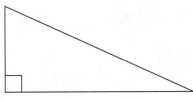

right triangle

Roman numerals

Number	Symbol	Number	Symbol	Number	Symbol
1	I	15	XV	150	CL
2	II	20	XX	200	CC
3	III	25	XXV	400	CD
4	IV	30	XXX	500	D
5	V	40	XL	600	DC
6	VI	50	L	900	CM
7	VII	60	LX	1,000	M
8	VIII	70	LXX	1,500	MD
9	IX	80	LXXX	1,900	MCM or
10	X	90	XC		MDCCCC
		100	C	1,930	MCMXXX
				1,963	MCMLXIII
				1,996	MCMXCVI
				2,000	MM

rounding   Eliminating the preciseness of a number. The number $151,284 could be rounded to $151,000 or $150,000 depending on the application. It allows the focus to be on the magnitude, not the preciseness, of the number. A number can be rounded up or down to the nearest number desired.

run chart   A simple time graph of points showing a trend, if any, in a series of events. For instance, the run chart of days people are absent shows that Monday is the most frequent day.

S-shaped curve   A curve that represents an event or a series of events, usually in a real-life situation, that is diagramed like a rough-shaped S. It could represent the sales of a best-selling book that increase dramatically at first but then level off.

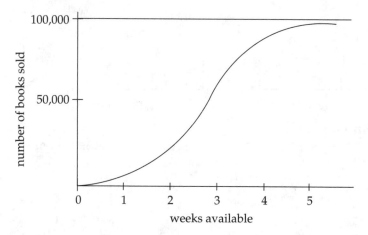

sample; sample distribution   A specific term in statistics that refers to a part of the whole range of what ever is being studied, as opposed to the entire population.

scalers   In science and engineering, quantities that have only magnitude (size) but not direction. An example of a scaler is the degrees of temperature. This is in contrast to a *vector*, which has magnitude and direction, such as wind velocity toward the northeast.

scatter diagram (scattergram or scatterplot)   A graph or plot of data, usually in the form of dots. This data in the aggregate can take on shapes, meaning there is a correlation, or the data can be randomly scattered meaning there is no correlation. See *regression line*.

scientific notation   Using exponents to represent very large numbers. For instance 2.5×10^9 equals 2,500,000,000.

semilogarithmic graph   Graphs that are logarithmic on one axis only, usually the y-axis.

sensitivity analysis   See *model*.

set   A mathematical expression including all elements of a group.

sigma   In statistics, the symbol for standard deviation. One sigma is one standard deviation. The small Greek letter sigma (σ) is used in statistical formulas to represent standard deviation. See *standard deviation*.

significance level or test   In statistics, the standard level of acceptance of correlations. That level of significance is usually .05 or .01, or to put it another way, a level that is either 95 percent or 99 percent accurate.

simple correlation or regression   A comparison or regression between just two variables. Multiple correlation or regression analysis compares many variables to find which are correlated, if any.

simple interest   Interest rates that do not compound, or earn interest on interest during the period. See *compound interest*

simplex method   A specific linear programming method that allows the solving of the more complex problems. It involves computational routines in an iterative process. See *linear programming.*

simplify   An algebraic operation that combines similar terms to condense it as much as possible.

simulation   A modeling technique used to represent a process or calculation.

six sigma   A statistical measurement of six standard deviations from the mean. Deviation in statistics is represented by the Greek letter sigma. It is commonly referred to in the new push toward manufacturing quality. The standard of six sigma specifies that there should only be 3.4 errors per million. Six standard deviations is namely 99.99976 percent of all the data values. Four sigma specifies 621 errors per million.

skewed distribution   A statistical distribution that is not centered, as is the typical bell-shaped curve or normal distribution. It is sometimes called *asymmetrical* because it tilts to one side or another. If the distribution is completely symmetrical, the mean, mode, and median are the same and the skewedness is zero. The distribution is said to be skewed to the right when the mean is to the right, or greater, than the mode. That is, the peak of the distribution is toward the left (which may seem counterintuitive). The distribution is skewed to the left when the mean is to the left, or less than, the mode and appears to *lean* to the right.

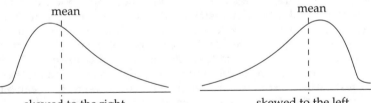

mean   mean

skewed to the right   skewed to the left

slope   The steepness of a graphed line. It is measured by the *rise over the run,* meaning the vertical distance divided by the horizontal distance.

smoothing   A statistical process of rounding values so that a clearer pattern of the data values may emerge.

spreadsheet   Computer software that allows for the input of data or a table of data that can be manipulated. Inputs are made to cells, which can be referenced by other cells. Rows are the horizontal entries, columns are vertical. The rows are usually numbers and the columns alphabetized. For instance, cell C7 is the C column and the seventh row. Formulas in cells can reference, manipulate, and calculate data from other cells. Business applications are numerous, such as in accounting, finance, sales, and marketing. The two most popular spreadsheet programs are Excel and Lotus 1-2-3.

square (of a number) The result of multiplying a number by itself. Two squared equals 4 (2 x 2 equals 4). It is written as $2^2 = 4$

square roots A factor of a number that when squared equals the number. For instance 4 is the square root of 16. It is written as: $\sqrt{16} = 4$

standard deviation One of the most common statistical measurements, measuring how data values are spread around the mean, or average, of the data. It is represented by the Greek letter sigma. One standard deviation is the measurement of approximately 68 percent (two-thirds) of the data values. Or, put another way, we expect that two-thirds of our data will fall within one standard deviation, in a normal distributions of data values. Two standard deviations capture approximately 95 percent (ninety-five hundreds) of the data. Three standard deviations capture approximately 99 percent of the data. See *sigma*.

standard error A statistical calculation determining how imperfect the sample is to the population. Also called the *standard error of estimate*.

statistic In statistics the mean or the standard deviation, or some other characteristic of the data, which describes a sample of the population; the term *parameter* describes the entire population of the distribution.

statistician A mathematician who studies the particular math of statistics, such as averages, standard deviations, and correlations.

statistics Mathematical methods that analyze, represent, and interpret numerical data. The mean, mode, and median measure the central tendencies of the distributions and the range, variance and standard deviation measure the variability of a distribution. The mathematics of statistics appears to have started in the late 1700s in London; the name comes from the word *statist*, an old word for statesman or politician. There are many mathematical, or statistical, methods that have been developed. To determine if two samples, or a sample and the population, are similar, there are several tests: The *t test* measures the difference between the means; the *F ratio* measures the difference between the variances or standard deviations; the *chi square test* measures differences of the frequencies. The *z score* measures the standard deviations from the mean.

stochastic A random variance is called stochastic. Stochastic modeling means using random numbers, within limits, to project results. Thus, if cash balances fluctuated across a range with uncertainty, using stochastic models you could account for all the possible values.

string formula A computer spreadsheet formula involving not only numerical values but statements and text as well.

student's t A statistical test between the *means* of two distributions to see how alike or not they are. It is also called the *t test, t distribution,* or the *t table.* It refers to testing the data for a certain level of confidence. William Grosset, a consultant to the Guinness Brewery in Dublin, wrote on this subject under the pseudonym *Student.* Perhaps he was embarrassed by working in a brewery. See *statistics.*

subtraction   Taking a value from another. The number being subtracted from is called the *subtrahend* and the number subtracted is called the *minuend.* For example, 5 (subtrahend) minus 3 (minuend) equals 2.

sum   The result of addition. The sum of 4 and 1 is 5.

symbols   Letter representations for mathematical processes or values. Mathematics and statistics are filled with them, often derived from the Greek alphabet. Examples are:

delta - Δ meaning a small increase

sigma - Σ meaning a sum

integral - ∫ used in calculus

t distribution or test   See *student's t.*

tangent (line)   The line that touches a circle, or curve, at only one point. A tangent line always forms a right angle to the radius of the circle at that point.

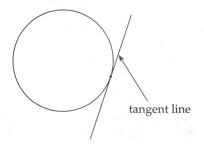

tangent line

theory   A systematic ordering of knowledge. A theory allows for the analysis and prediction of outcomes. The Modern Portfolio Theory allows for the analysis and prediction of investment results, for example.

time value of money   Financial calculations of present and future value. Time makes a difference in the value of something, such as an investment. If you were promised $1,000 in three years, but instead you wanted the money now, it would only be worth $863 now if the rate of investment was 5 percent. The time of three years was the difference between then and now. If you invested the $863 now at 5 percent, in three years it would be $1,000.

time-series analysis   The analysis of data over time, such as monthly or yearly. Examples are the analysis of a company's earnings over time, monthly retail store sales, or daily prices on the stock market.

today's dollars   How much something in the past or future is valued today, if it were valued in today's dollars. Also called *present-day dollars.* It often is used with the rate of inflation to illustrate how costs have risen. If, for example, with an inflation rate of 3 percent, the actual cost of a loaf of bread in ten years would be $2.08, in today's dollars it is worth $1.55. That is, something that costs $1.55 today, but increases by 3 percent for ten years, then costs $2.08. See *present value*.

triangle   A three-sided geometric figure. An isosceles triangle has two sides of equal length; a right triangle has one angle that is right, or 90°; a scalene triangle has no two sides equal and no angles at a right angle.

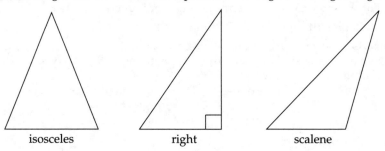

isosceles   right   scalene

two-tailed test   In statistics, the testing for both ends, or tails, of the distribution curve. This is in contrast to testing only one side for statistical significance.

variable   A changing value. Or, as a mathematician would say, the replacement set containing more than one element. In an algebraic formula a variable is often represented with letters like x or y. See *dependent and independent variables*. Also see *constant*.

vectors   In science and engineering there are many quantities that have magnitude (size) as well as direction. An example of a vector is wind velocity—15 m.p.h. blowing toward the northeast. This is in contrast to a *scaler*, which is magnitude only—the temperature today is 65°.

Venn diagram   A diagram representing two or more sets of numbers and illustrating how they are combined or not. It is usually shown as circles inside a rectangle. Each circle represents a set of numbers. If the circles have some overlap, those parts are common to both. Named after John Venn (1824-1923).

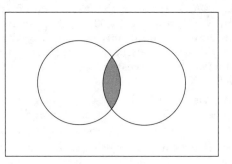

volatility   The amount of variation or fluctuation of something. An example is the volatility of the stock market. The more volatility the greater the risk, or uncertainty.

weighted average   An average where each item is multiplied by a *weight* or factor relative to the whole.

whole number   The set of counting numbers including 0.

x-axis   In graphing, the horizontal axis. See *y-axis*.

y-axis   In graphing, the vertical axis. See *x-axis*.

z-axis   In graphing three dimensions, the additional dimension from the x- and y-axis. See *x-axis* and *y-axis*.

z score or measure   In statistics, the measurement of the number of standard deviations. A z score of 2 means 2 standard deviations from the mean, or average.

zero   Neither positive nor negative; nothing. As a mathematician would say, it is an element that when added to a number results in the number itself.

Index

ABOUT THE AUTHOR

Paul Westbrook is a noted financial and retirement planning expert who has been quoted frequently in major publications. He began his career in business as a human resource professional with several major corporations, then moved on to consulting where he started and headed a national practice in financial and retirement planning with a major international benefits consulting firm. Paul runs his own financial and retirement planning firm in Ridgewood, New Jersey and also gives seminars and speeches on related topics. Paul's initial major in college was math and science, subjects he still loves.